The
Anatomy
Student's Self-test
Colouring Book

The Anatomy
Student's Self-test
Colouring Book

Second Edition

Revised, expanded, and updated edition

Consultant Editor: **Professor Ken Ashwell** BMedSc, MBBS, PhD

QUAD BOOKS

Inspiring | Educating | Creating | Entertaining

Brimming with creative inspiration, how-to projects, and useful information to enrich your everyday life, Quarto Knows is a favourite destination for those pursuing their interests and passions. Visit our site and dig deeper with our books into your area of interest: Quarto Creates, Quarto Cooks, Quarto Homes, Quarto Lives, Quarto Drives, Quarto Explores, Quarto Gifts, or Quarto Kids.

First edition published 2007 by Global Book Publishing Pty Ltd.
This revised edition © 2018 Quarto Publishing plc

Conceived, designed and produced by Global Book Publishing,
an imprint of The Quarto Group, The Old Brewery, 6 Blundell Street, London N7 9BH, UK
T (0) 20 7700 6700 **F** (0) 20 7700 8066 **www.QuartoKnows.com**

ISBN: 978-0-85762-594-6

CONSULTANT EDITOR   Ken Ashwell, BMEdSc, MBBS, PhD

CONTRIBUTORS   Robin Arnold, MSc
Deborah Bryce, BSc, MScQual, Mchiro, CrCertHEd
John Gallo, MB, BS(Hons), FRACP, FRCPA
Rakesh Kumar, MB, BS, PhD
Peter Lavelle, MB, BS
Karen McGhee, BSc
Michael Roberts, MB, BS, LLB(Hons)
Emeritus Professor Frederick Rost,
    BSc(Med), MB, BS, PhD, DCP(London), DipRMS
Elizabeth Tancred, BSc, PhD
Dzung Vu, MD, MB, BS, DipAnat, GradCertHEd
Phil Waite, BSc(Hons), MBChB, CertHEd, PhD

ILLUSTRATORS   Mike Gorman, Thomson Digital, Glen Vause,
Medical Artist Ltd (www.medical-artist.com)

Printed in China

Contents

Introduction

Many of us are fascinated by the internal structure and workings of our bodies. However, we see only a little of that at the level of the skin, where bony prominences and soft tissues lie close to the surface. Delving below the skin to find out how tissues and organs nestle together and perform their daily functions gives us an insight into a remarkable internal world that we often take for granted in our day-to-day lives. Everyone who has the opportunity to study human anatomy will take away some fascinating perceptions that will stay with them for the rest of their lives, whatever their occupation.

All students of anatomy need three key resources: i) a comprehensive textbook, ii) a quality atlas, and, importantly, iii) a book like this to test and reinforce anatomical knowledge. The strength of a colouring-in and labelling workbook such as this is that it requires active learning. By this we mean the dynamic engagement of the student with the subject, in such a way that the recall of declarative facts and three-dimensional knowledge of the shape, position, and relations of structures are continuously put to the test. This is something that cannot be obtained by passively reading a textbook or reflexively browsing an atlas or software resource.

Students should colour the anatomical diagrams within these pages, preferably using red for arteries, blue for veins, yellow for nerves, and green for lymphatic channels. By colouring the structures, you will be imprinting their shape and relationship on your mind. By labelling each structure and checking your answers against the key at the bottom of the page, you will be impressing the word and its spelling on your mind in a far more effective way than by simply reading a textbook.

How This Book Is Organised

This workbook is divided into 16 thoroughly illustrated chapters covering introductory information, the structures of all the organ systems, and the relationships between them. Understanding these anatomical relationships is critically important to good clinical examination and comprehension of disease processes. This new edition includes clinical points text boxes to illustrate the medical significance of the structures under study. (The medical information given within those boxes is intended for education only and does not replace consultation with a medical professional.)

This book will be an invaluable resource for all those who study anatomy for their professional careers – whether in medicine, physical therapy, nursing, exercise science, allied health, nutrition, or fitness – as well as members of the general public who are curious about what lies beneath their skin.

Professor Ken Ashwell

How to Use This Book

This book is designed to assist students and professionals to identify body parts and structures, and the coloured leader lines aid the process by clearly pointing out each body part. The functions of colouring and labelling allow you to familiarise yourself with individual parts of the body and then check your knowledge.

Colouring is best done using either pencils or ballpoint pens (not felt-tip pens) in a variety of dark and light colours. Where possible, you should use the same colour for like structures, so that all completed illustrations can be utilised later as visual references. According to anatomical convention, the colour green is usually reserved for lymphatic structures, yellow for nerves, red for arteries, and blue for veins.

Labelling the coloured leader lines that point to separate parts of the illustration enables you to test and then check your knowledge using the answers that are printed at the bottom of the page.

CHAPTER NAME

SPREAD TITLE

HEADINGS
Illustration headings give the name of the body part and the orientation.

LOCATOR DIAGRAMS
Locator diagrams show the position and orientation of a cross-section illustration.

ILLUSTRATIONS
Illustrations may show a whole body system, a single organ, or the microstructure of a body part. In some instances, the illustrator has removed one part of the body so that another may be viewed more clearly; for example, in some of the illustrations of the abdominal organs the liver has been peeled back to show the gallbladder. In some cases a dashed line has been used to show where one structure lies behind or beneath another.

TEXT
The text includes essential information about the body part or system.

ANSWERS
The missing labels are presented upside down, in numerical order.

LABELS
Numbered blank lines allow space for the name of the individual structure to be written in. The sequence runs anticlockwise, usually starting on the left side of each illustration.

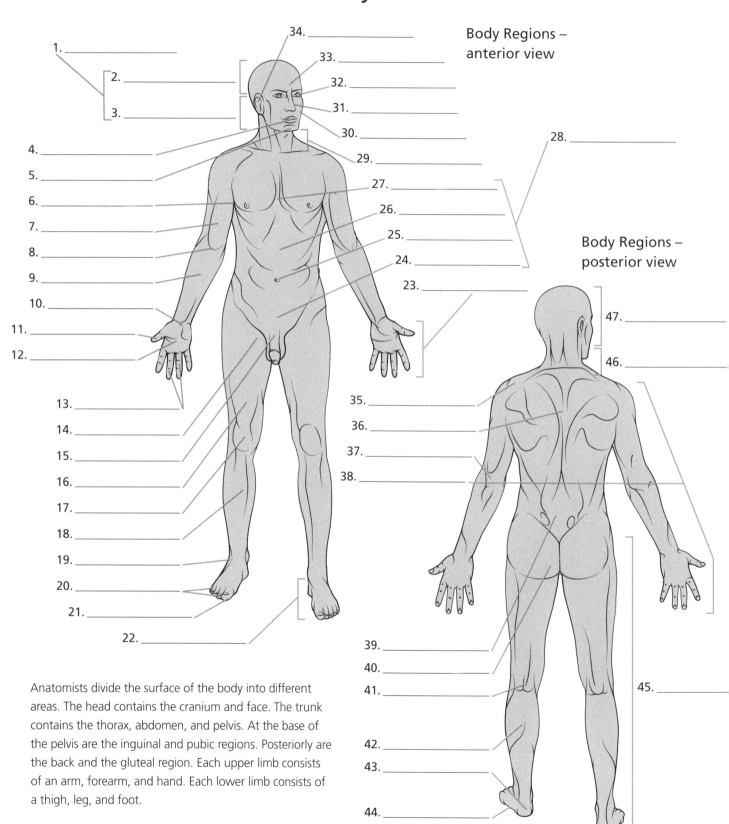

Overview of the Human Body

1. _____

2. _____

3. _____

4. _____

5. _____

6. _____

7. _____

8. _____

9. _____

10. _____

11. _____

12. _____

13. _____

14. _____

15. _____

16. _____

17. _____

18. _____

19. _____

20. _____

21. _____

22. _____

34. _____

33. _____

32. _____

31. _____

30. _____

29. _____

27. _____

26. _____

25. _____

24. _____

23. _____

35. _____

36. _____

37. _____

38. _____

Body Regions – anterior view

28. _____

Body Regions – posterior view

47. _____

46. _____

45. _____

39. _____

40. _____

41. _____

42. _____

43. _____

44. _____

Anatomists divide the surface of the body into different areas. The head contains the cranium and face. The trunk contains the thorax, abdomen, and pelvis. At the base of the pelvis are the inguinal and pubic regions. Posteriorly are the back and the gluteal region. Each upper limb consists of an arm, forearm, and hand. Each lower limb consists of a thigh, leg, and foot.

Answers

1. Head, 2. Cranium (cranial), 3. Face (facial), 4. Mouth (oral), 5. Chin (mental), 6. Axilla (axillary), 7. Brachium (brachial), 8. Elbow (anterobrachial), 9. Antebrachium (antebrachial), 10. Wrist (carpal), 11. Pollex (thumb), 12. Palm (palmar), 13. Digits (digital or phalangeal), 14. Inguen (inguinal), 15. Pubis (pubic), 16. Femur (femoral), 17. Patella (patellar), 18. Crus (crural), 19. Tarsus (tarsal), 20. Digits (digital or phalangeal), 21. Hallux (big toe), 22. Pes (pedal), 23. Hand, 24. Pelvis (pelvic), 25. Umbilicus (umbilical), 26. Abdomen (abdominal), 27. Thorax (thoracic), 28. Trunk, 29. Neck (cervical), 30. Cheek (buccal), 31. Nose (nasal), 32. Eye (orbital or ocular), 33. Forehead (frontal), 34. Ear (otic), 35. Shoulder (acromial), 36. Back (dorsal), 37. Olecranon (olecranal), 38. Upper limb, 39. Lower back (lumbar), 40. Gluteus (gluteal), 41. Popliteus (popliteal), 42. Sura (sural), 43. Calcaneus (calcaneal), 44. Sole (plantar), 45. Lower limb, 46. Neck (cervical), 47. Head

The body cavities are spaces containing the internal organs (viscera). The main cavities are the thoracic and abdominopelvic cavities in the torso and the cranial cavity in the head. The thoracic (or chest) cavity contains the heart, lungs, trachea, and oesophagus. The abdominopelvic cavity is divided into the abdominal cavity, which contains most of the gastrointestinal tract, the kidneys, and the adrenal glands; below the abdominal cavity, the pelvic cavity contains the urogenital system and the rectum. The cranial cavity contains the brain and extends caudally as the spinal canal.

Body Cavities – sagittal view

10. _____

1. _____

2. _____

3. _____

5. _____

4. _____

6. _____

8. _____

7. _____

View Orientation and Anatomical Planes

Specific terms describe the orientation and relationships of the body and its parts. Sections of the body are described in terms of anatomical planes (flat surfaces). These are imaginary lines – vertical or horizontal – drawn through a body in the anatomical position (that is, with the body standing erect, feet together with toes pointed forwards, and arms at the sides with palms facing forwards). A transverse (axial or horizontal) plane cuts the body across from side to side, separating superior areas above from inferior areas below. A coronal (frontal) plane divides the body into dorsal (posterior, or back) and ventral (anterior, or front) pieces. A sagittal plane separates one side of the body from the other side (left from right). The midsagittal (median) plane is the sagittal plane exactly in the middle of the body. The relationships of one body part to another are identified by terms such as medial (towards the midline of the body) or lateral (away from the midline of the body); inferior (below, or lower) or superior (upper, or above); cranial (towards the head) or caudal (towards the tail); anterior (ventral, or towards the front) or posterior (dorsal, or towards the back); proximal (closer to a reference point) or distal (farther from that reference point).

12. _Superior_

Anatomical View Orientation

11. _medial_

10. _posterior_

9. _lateral_

8. _dorsal_

7. _palmar_

6. _inferior_

1. _anterior_

2. _proximal_

3. _distal_

4. _dorsal_

5. _plantar_

Answers

Anatomical Planes

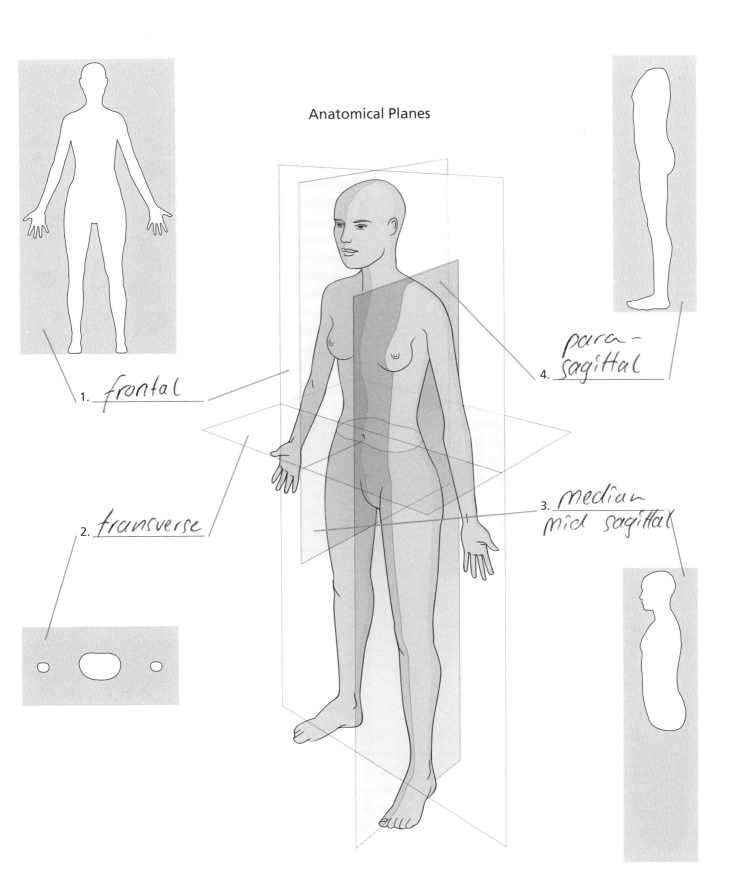

1. *frontal*

2. *transverse*

3. *median mid sagittal*

4. *para-sagittal*

Answers

Cell Structure and Major Cell Types

1. _____

2. _____

3. _____

4. _____

5. _____

6. _____

14. _____

13. _____

12. _____

11. _____

10. _____

9. _____

8. _____

7. _____

Cell Structure

Cells are the basic units of the body. Every adult body contains more than 100 million million cells. Cells are surrounded by a cell membrane. Within the cell membrane lies the cytoplasm, a fluid containing many important structural units called organelles. These include rough endoplasmic reticulum, mitochondria, Golgi apparatus, and centrioles. The nucleus is separated from the cytoplasm by a nuclear membrane. Cells are specialised to perform particular functions. Neurons are specialised cells that conduct nerve impulses. Each has three main parts: the cell body, branching projections (dendrites) that carry impulses to the cell body, and one elongated projection (axon) that conveys impulses away from the cell body.

15. _____

16. _____

Neuron

17. _____

18. _____

24. _____

23. _____

22. _____

21. _____

20. _____

19. _____

Answers

Haemoglobin

1. _____

2. _____

5. _____

6. _____

7. _____

4. _____

3. _____

Megakaryocyte

Blood Cells

8. _____

9. _____   10. _____

Blood is made up of two broad types of cells (red and white blood cells) and specialised cell fragments called platelets. Red blood cells are the most numerous cells in the body. The fully mature red cell extrudes its nucleus and appears in the circulation full of haemoglobin. Its shape is that of a biconcave disc. Haemoglobin carries oxygen to the tissues. Known also as leukocytes, white blood cells are produced in red bone marrow and lymphatic tissue. They defend the body from viruses, bacteria and other microbes, and invertebrate parasites. There are five major types: neutrophils, eosinophils, basophils, monocytes, and lymphocytes. Platelets are the smallest structural units in the blood. They are formed in the bone marrow from the cytoplasm of giant cells known as megakaryocytes.

11. _____   12. _____   13. _____

Answers

Tissues (cellular level)

1. _____

2. _____

3. _____

4. _____

5. _____

6. _____

Loose
Connective
Tissue

9. _____

8. _____

7. _____

Tissue is a group or layer of cells, plus the material packed between them, all of which function together for the same specialised purpose. There are four major types of tissues in the body: connective, epithelial, neural, and muscular. Connective tissue is tissue made up of cells and protein fibres arranged in a framework that provides support for other body tissues and holds them together. Humans have five main types of connective tissue: loose connective tissue (including adipose tissue), dense connective tissue, cartilage, bone, and blood. Epithelial tissue is made up of cells that are packed very closely together. The cells are arranged in continuous sheets in either single or multiple layers. Neural tissue is composed of two main types of cells: neuroglia and neurons. The glial cells, which are usually smaller and far more abundant, provide support and protection for the neurons. Muscle tissue is made up of cells that contract.

Adipose Tissue

Bone Tissue

11. _____

17. _____

16. _____

15. _____

10. _____

12. _____

13. _____

Epithelial Tissue   14. _____   Neural Tissue

Answers

Muscle Tissue

1. *Skeletal*

2. *cardiac*

3. *Smooth*

Cartilage Tissue

4. _____

5. _____

6. _____

Dense Regular Connective Tissue

Muscle tissue is composed of cells that are purpose-built for contraction. There are three main forms: skeletal, cardiac, and smooth. The muscle fibres, or myofibres, of skeletal muscle are long and cylindrical, are arranged parallel to each other, and have a striped appearance under the microscope. Cardiac muscle cells are similar in that they too have a striped appearance. They, however, are branched. Smooth muscle tissue has no striations. One type of dense connective tissue, known as dense regular connective tissue, forms tendons, ligaments, and cartilage. Another, elastic connective tissue, is specialised for stretching. Cartilage comes in three forms: hyaline cartilage, fibrocartilage, and elastic cartilage. Hyaline cartilage covers the bones where they form synovial joints. Fibrocartilage forms a component of some other joints, which usually have a limited range of movement. Elastic cartilage is the hard material that can be felt in the external ear.

7. _____

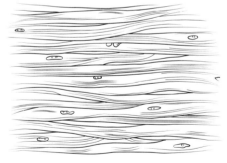

8. _____

Answers

1. Skeletal muscle tissue, 2. Cardiac muscle tissue, 3. Smooth muscle tissue, 4. Hyaline cartilage, 5. Fibrocartilage, 6. Elastic cartilage, 7. Tendon tissue, 8. Ligament tissue

Integumentary System

The skin is a protective organ that covers the body, merging with mucous membranes at the openings of the body such as the mouth and anus. Specialised nerve receptors in the skin also allow the body to sense pain, hot and cold, touch, and pressure. Skin is composed of two layers: the epidermis and the dermis. The epidermis is the outer protective layer. The deepest layers of the epidermis are the basal and spinous layers (the stratum granulosum and stratum spinosum, respectively); the outer layer is the horny layer (or stratum corneum). The dermis is the skin's inner layer and contains networks of blood vessels and nerves. Beneath the dermis is a layer of fat cells. Among the layers of the epidermis and the dermis are the specialised structures: hair follicles, sweat glands, and sebaceous glands. Hair and nails are made mainly from a tough, hard protein called keratin produced in the deeper layers of the skin's epidermis.

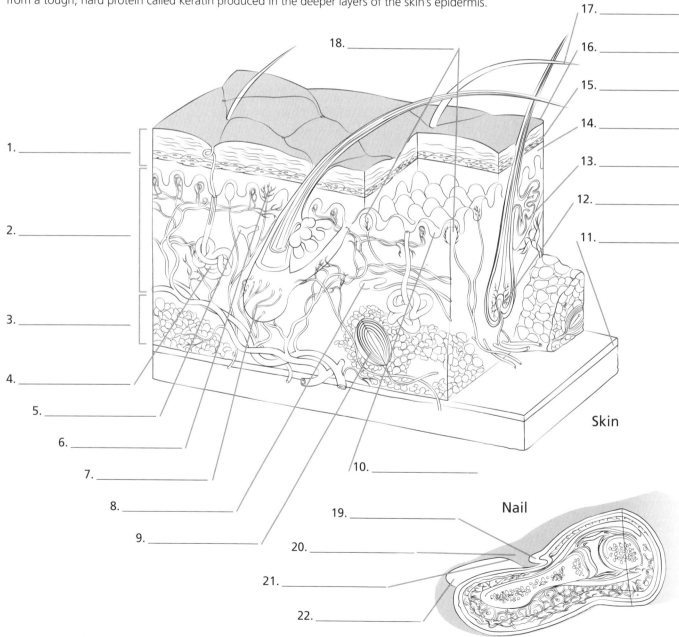

17. _____

16. _____

15. _____

14. _____

13. _____

12. _____

11. _____

18. _____

1. _____

2. _____

3. _____

4. _____

5. _____

6. _____

7. _____

8. _____

9. _____

10. _____

Skin

19. _____

20. _____

21. _____

22. _____

Nail

Answers

1. Epidermis, 2. Dermis, 3. Subcutaneous fat, 4. Sweat gland, 5. Ruffini endings, 6. Free nerve ending, 7. Nerve ending, 8. Krause bulb, 9. Pacinian corpuscle, 10. Dermal papilla, 11. Deep fascia, 12. Hair follicle, 13. Sebaceous gland, 14. Stratum spinosum, 15. Stratum granulosum, 16. Stratum corneum, 17. Hair, 18. Meissner corpuscles, 19. Root of nail, 20. Cuticle, 21. Lunula, 22. Nail

Hair

1. _____

2. _____

3. _____

4. _____

5. _____

6. _____

7. _____

18. _____

17. _____

16. _____

15. _____

14. _____

13. _____

12. _____

11. _____

10. _____

9. _____

8. _____

Hair is made of keratin and has a fine thread-like structure, consisting of a root, embedded in the skin, and a shaft, projecting from the skin surface. The root ends in a soft whitish enlargement, the hair bulb, which is lodged in an elongated pit in the skin called the follicle. Short fine hair covers most of the body, with some areas more densely covered – the adult human scalp contains about one hundred thousand hair follicles. The scalp is the skin and connective tissue covering the skull. The skin is attached to the skull by the loose areolar tissue and the pericranium.

25. _____

24. _____

23. _____

22. _____

21. _____

20. _____

19. _____

Scalp

Answers

Skeletal System

Skeletal System – anterior view

1. frontal
2. parietal
3. temporal
4. maxilla
5. cervical v.
6. costal cartilage
7. true rib
8. thoracic v.
9. false rib
10. lumbar v.
11. sacrum transverse process
12. ilium
13. sacrum
14. coccyx
15. ischium
16. pubic symphysis
17. tarsals

39. orbit
38.
37.
36.
35. mandible
34. clavicle
33. sternum
32. humerus
31. 12th rib floating
30. radius
29. ulna
28. metacarpals
27. phalanges
26. metacarpals
25. pubis
24. femur
23. patella
22. tibia
21. fibula
20. talus
19. metatarsals
18. phalanges

The skeleton is the framework of the body, supporting it and protecting the internal organs. The skeleton is usually described in two parts: the axial skeleton and the appendicular skeleton. The axial skeleton consists of the skull, the vertebral column, and the thoracic cage. The appendicular skeleton consists of the bones of the limbs, and the shoulder and pelvic girdles. Bone is rigid calcified tissue. Wherever two bones come into contact, there is a joint (or a suture, for adjoining bones of the skull). The bones may be separated by cartilage or fluid. Within the body, there is a range of joint types – ball-and-socket, ellipsoidal, hinge, gliding, pivot, and saddle – each offering a different range of movement. Joints are supported and strengthened by ligaments (tough, white, fibrous, slightly elastic tissues).

Answers

1. Frontal bone, 2. Parietal bone, 3. Temporal bone, 4. Maxilla, 5. Cervical vertebra, 6. Costal cartilage, 7. True rib, 8. Thoracic vertebra, 9. False rib, 10. Lumbar vertebra, 11. Transverse process, 12. Ilium, 13. Sacrum, 14. Coccyx, 15. Ischium, 16. Symphysis pubis, 17. Tarsal bones, 18. Phalanges, 19. Metatarsal bones, 20. Talus, 21. Fibula, 22. Tibia, 23. Patella, 24. Femur, 25. Pubic bone, 26. Metacarpal bones, 27. Phalanges, 28. Carpal bones, 29. Ulna, 30. Radius, 31. Twelfth rib (floating rib), 32. Humerus, 33. Sternum, 34. Clavicle, 35. Mandible, 36. Lower teeth, 37. Upper teeth, 38. Anterior nasal aperture, 39. Orbit

Skeletal System – posterior view

1. _____
2. _____
3. _____
4. _____
5. _____
6. _____
7. _____
8. _____
9. _____
10. _____
11. _____
12. _____
13. _____
14. _____

Skeletal System – lateral view

35. _____
34. _____
33. _____
32. _____
31. _____
30. _____
43. _____
29. _____
28. _____
27. _____
42. _____
41. _____
26. _____
25. _____
24. _____
23. _____
40. _____
21. _____
22. _____
20. _____
19. _____
39. _____
18. _____
17. _____
16. _____
38. _____
37. _____
15. _____
36. _____

Answers

Bone Structure

Bone is a type of connective tissue and, as such, is composed of cells in a matrix. The major components of the matrix include mineral salts and collagen fibres. Four types of cells are present: osteoprogenitor cells, osteoblasts, osteocytes, and osteoclasts. A typical mature long bone has a central shaft – the diaphysis – and ends known as epiphyses. Inside the diaphysis is the medulla, which contains bone marrow and is lined with endosteum – a layer rich in osteoprogenitor cells and osteoclasts. The diaphysis meets the epiphysis at the metaphysis. Most of the bone is protected and nourished by the periosteum – a membrane served by nerves and blood vessels that enter the bone.

Bone Structure – cross-sectional view of the femoral head

1. _____
2. _____
3. _____
4. _____
5. _____
6. _____
7. _____
8. _____
9. _____
10. _____
11. _____
12. _____
13. _____
14. _____
15. _____
16. _____

Answers

1. Spongy bone, 2. Muscle, 3. Tendon, 4. Epiphyseal plate, 5. Marrow cavity, 6. Bone marrow, 7. Cortical bone, 8. Periosteum, 9. Endosteum, 10. Inner circumferential lamella, 11. Volkmann's canal, 12. Interstitial lamellae, 13. Outer circumferential lamellae, 14. Concentric lamellae, 15. Haversian canals, 16. Trabecula of spongy bone

Bones of the Skull

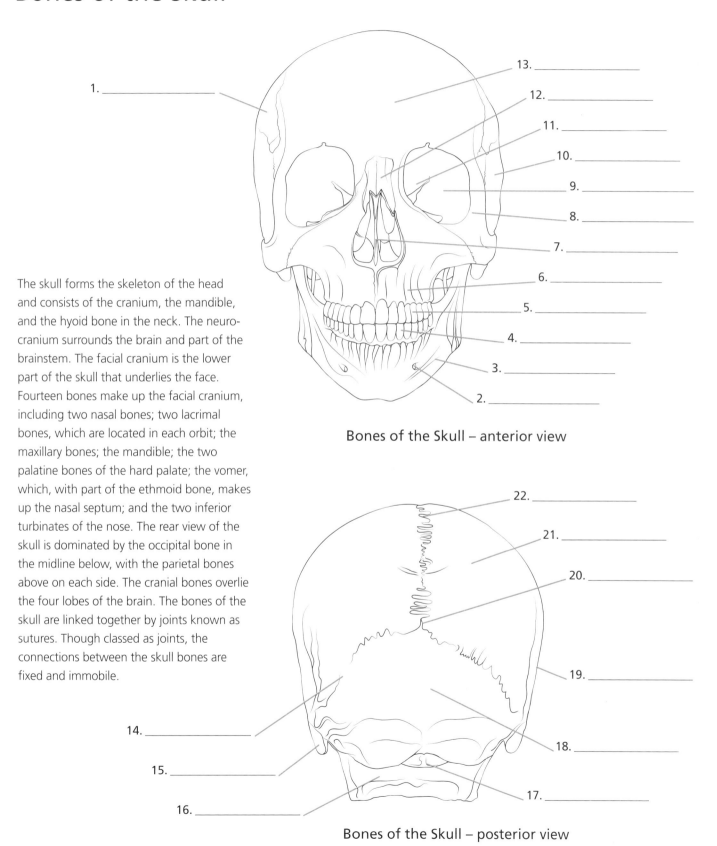

1. _____

13. _____
12. _____
11. _____
10. _____
9. _____
8. _____
7. _____
6. _____
5. _____
4. _____
3. _____
2. _____

Bones of the Skull – anterior view

The skull forms the skeleton of the head and consists of the cranium, the mandible, and the hyoid bone in the neck. The neuro-cranium surrounds the brain and part of the brainstem. The facial cranium is the lower part of the skull that underlies the face. Fourteen bones make up the facial cranium, including two nasal bones; two lacrimal bones, which are located in each orbit; the maxillary bones; the mandible; the two palatine bones of the hard palate; the vomer, which, with part of the ethmoid bone, makes up the nasal septum; and the two inferior turbinates of the nose. The rear view of the skull is dominated by the occipital bone in the midline below, with the parietal bones above on each side. The cranial bones overlie the four lobes of the brain. The bones of the skull are linked together by joints known as sutures. Though classed as joints, the connections between the skull bones are fixed and immobile.

22. _____
21. _____
20. _____
19. _____
18. _____
17. _____

14. _____
15. _____
16. _____

Bones of the Skull – posterior view

Answers

Bones of the Skull

In a lateral view, the division of the skull into the larger ovoid brain case (neurocranium) and the smaller triangular face (facial cranium) is evident. The orbits are pyramidal spaces (tapering dorsally) on either side of the face. At the sides of the skull, the temporal bones contain a system of spaces, which form the middle and inner parts of the ears. A sagittal view of the skull reveals the interrelationship of the bones of both the neurocranium and the face. The bones of the skull enclose several spaces. The largest cavity accommodates the brain. The nasal cavities are chambers that are connected to paranasal sinuses in the frontal, ethmoid, maxillary, and sphenoid bones. The major bones of the neurocranium are the occipital, parietal, temporal, and frontal bones.

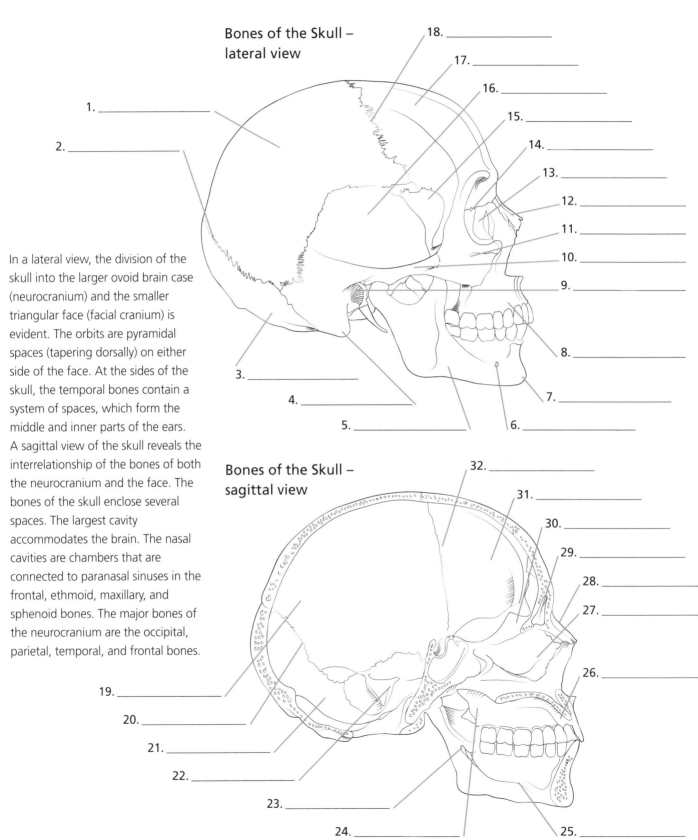

Bones of the Skull –
lateral view

18. _____
17. _____
16. _____
15. _____
14. _____
13. _____
12. _____
11. _____
10. _____
9. _____
8. _____
7. _____
6. _____
5. _____
4. _____
3. _____
2. _____
1. _____

Bones of the Skull –
sagittal view

32. _____
31. _____
30. _____
29. _____
28. _____
27. _____
26. _____
25. _____
24. _____
23. _____
22. _____
21. _____
20. _____
19. _____

Answers

A number of bones, both neurocranial and facial cranial, come together to form the base of the skull. The base of the skull contains a number of foramina, through which the spinal cord, cranial nerves, and blood vessels enter or exit. The large hole in the occipital bone, the foramen magnum, is for the passage of the spinal cord.

1. _____

2. _____

3. _____

4. _____

5. _____

6. _____

7. _____

8. _____

9. _____

10. _____

11. _____

12. _____

13. _____

14. _____

15. _____

16. _____

Base of the Skull – inferior view

Answers

Bones of the Head and Face

The jaw consists of two parts: a movable lower jaw, formed by the mandible, and a fixed upper jaw, formed by the maxillary bones. The mandible articulates with the temporal bones on each side at the temporomandibular joints. These joints are reinforced by a capsule and strong ligaments. The teeth are bony structures embedded in the upper and lower jaws. The cavities for the eyes, called the orbits, are formed by the frontal, ethmoid, lacrimal, zygomatic, nasal, palatine, sphenoid, and maxillary bones. The bones that form the outer wall and roof of the orbit are thick and strong, whereas the bones that form the inner walls are thin and fragile.

Bones of the Jaw – lateral view

1. _____
2. _____
3. _____
4. _____
5. _____
6. _____
7. _____
8. _____
9. _____
10. _____
11. _____
12. _____
13. _____

Ligaments of the Jaw – lateral view

Orbital Cavity – superior view

14. _____
15. _____
16. _____
17. _____
18. _____
19. _____
20. _____
21. _____
22. _____
23. _____
24. _____

Answers

1. Mastoid process, 2. Mandible, 3. Mental foramen, 4. Mental protuberance, 5. Maxilla, 6. Pterygoid process of sphenoid bone, 7. Zygomatic process of temporal bone, 8. Zygomatic bone, 9. Nasal bone, 10. Lacrimal bone, 11. Ethmoid bone, 12. Greater wing of sphenoid bone, 13. Squamous part of temporal bone, 14. Styloid process, 15. Stylomandibular ligament, 16. Sphenomandibular ligament, 17. Lateral (temporomandibular) ligament, 18. Lateral (temporomandibular) ligament, 19. Frontal bone, 20. Temporal bone, 21. Ethmoid bone, 22. Cibriform plate of ethmoid bone, 23. Eyeball, 24. Frontal sinus

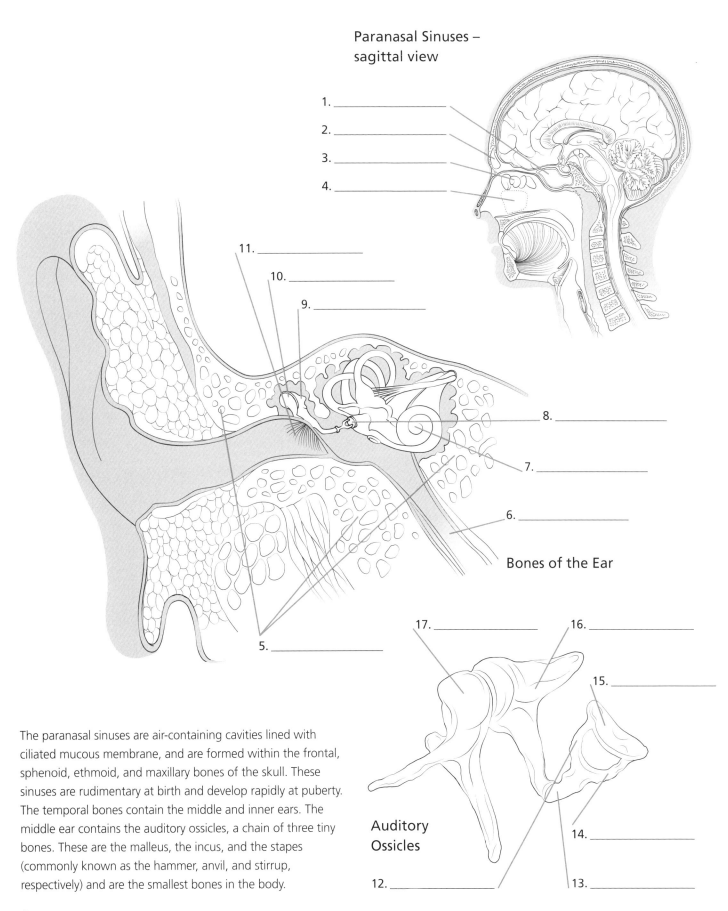

Paranasal Sinuses – sagittal view

1. _____
2. _____
3. _____
4. _____

11. _____
10. _____
9. _____

8. _____
7. _____
6. _____

Bones of the Ear

5. _____

17. _____   16. _____

15. _____

14. _____

Auditory Ossicles

12. _____   13. _____

The paranasal sinuses are air-containing cavities lined with ciliated mucous membrane, and are formed within the frontal, sphenoid, ethmoid, and maxillary bones of the skull. These sinuses are rudimentary at birth and develop rapidly at puberty. The temporal bones contain the middle and inner ears. The middle ear contains the auditory ossicles, a chain of three tiny bones. These are the malleus, the incus, and the stapes (commonly known as the hammer, anvil, and stirrup, respectively) and are the smallest bones in the body.

Answers

1. Sphenoidal sinus, 2. Frontal sinus, 3. Ethmoid sinuses, 4. Maxillary sinus, 5. Temporal bone, 6. Eustachian (auditory) tube, 7. Cochlea, 8. Stapes, 9. Incus, 10. Malleus, 11. Tympanic membrane (eardrum), 12. Anterior crus of stapes, 13. Stapes, 14. Posterior crus of stapes, 15. Footplate of stapes, 16. Incus, 17. Malleus

Vertebral Column

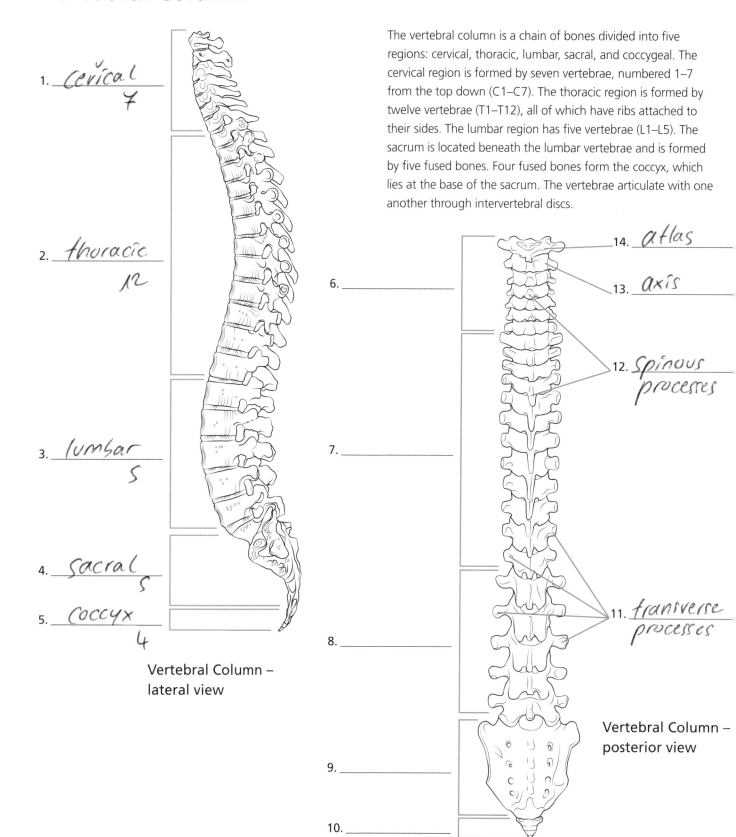

1. cerical
   7

2. thoracic
   12

3. lumbar
   5

4. sacral
   5

5. coccyx
   4

Vertebral Column –
lateral view

The vertebral column is a chain of bones divided into five regions: cervical, thoracic, lumbar, sacral, and coccygeal. The cervical region is formed by seven vertebrae, numbered 1–7 from the top down (C1–C7). The thoracic region is formed by twelve vertebrae (T1–T12), all of which have ribs attached to their sides. The lumbar region has five vertebrae (L1–L5). The sacrum is located beneath the lumbar vertebrae and is formed by five fused bones. Four fused bones form the coccyx, which lies at the base of the sacrum. The vertebrae articulate with one another through intervertebral discs.

14. atlas

13. axis

12. spinous processes

11. transverse processes

6. _____

7. _____

8. _____

9. _____

10. _____

Vertebral Column –
posterior view

Answers

Cervical Vertebrae:
Atlas (C1) – superior view

1. _____
2. _____
3. _____
4. _____
5. _____
6. _____
7. _____
8. _____
9. _____

10. _____
11. _____
12. _____

The same basic elements are found in most vertebrae: a vertebral body, a vertebral arch comprising two pedicles and two laminae, and processes that project away from the arch. The bodies lie in front and are weight-bearing. They increase in size as they progress down the spine. The pedicles form the side walls of the vertebral foramen (spinal canal), and the two laminae form the back walls. The atlas and axis are specialised vertebrae. The first cervical vertebra, the atlas (C1), is a bony ring, and unlike the other vertebrae, it does not have a body or spinous process. The axis (C2) sits beneath the atlas, forming a pivot joint (the atlantoaxial joint) where the two vertebrae meet.

18. _____
17. _____
16. _____
15. _____

Cervical Vertebrae: Atlas (C1)
and Axis (C2) – oblique view

13. _____
14. _____

25. _____
24. _____
23. _____
22. _____
21. _____

19. _____
20. _____

Cervical Vertebrae:
Axis (C2) – superior view

Answers

1. Anterior tubercle, 2. Anterior arch, 3. Articular facet for dens, 4. Vertebral foramen, 5. Posterior arch, 6. Posterior tubercle, 7. Superior articular process, 8. Transverse foramen, 9. Transverse process, 10. Anterior tubercle of atlas, 11. Anterior arch of atlas, 12. Transverse foramen of atlas, 13. Transverse process of axis, 14. Inferior articular process, 15. Spinous process of axis, 16. Posterior tubercle of atlas, 17. Body of axis, 18. Dens of axis, 19. Transverse foramen, 20. Spinous process, 21. Vertebral foramen, 22. Body of axis, 23. Dens of axis, 24. Superior articular facet, 25. Facet for atlas

Vertebral Column

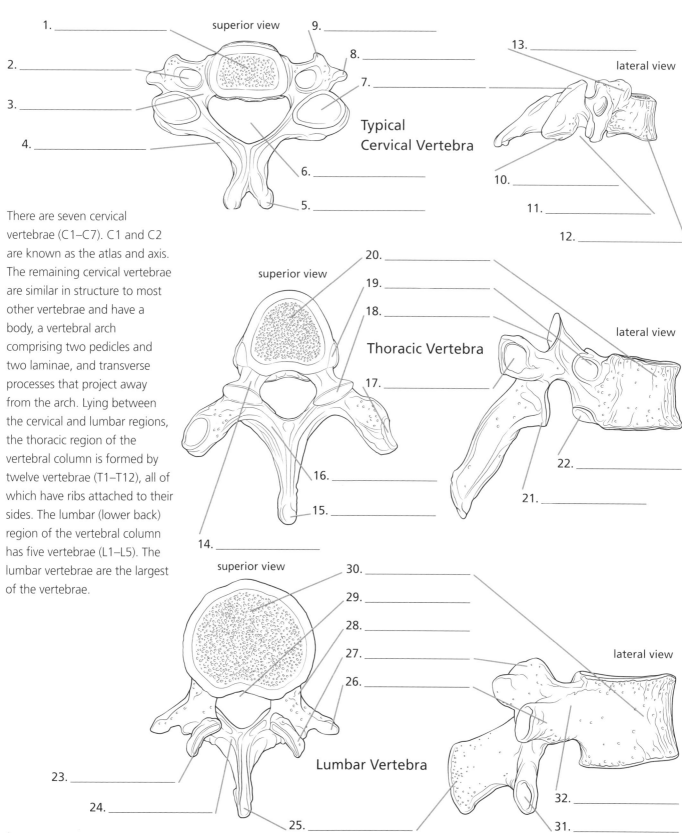

superior view

Typical
Cervical Vertebra

lateral view

1. _____

2. _____

3. _____

4. _____

5. _____

6. _____

7. _____

8. _____

9. _____

10. _____

11. _____

12. _____

13. _____

There are seven cervical vertebrae (C1–C7). C1 and C2 are known as the atlas and axis. The remaining cervical vertebrae are similar in structure to most other vertebrae and have a body, a vertebral arch comprising two pedicles and two laminae, and transverse processes that project away from the arch. Lying between the cervical and lumbar regions, the thoracic region of the vertebral column is formed by twelve vertebrae (T1–T12), all of which have ribs attached to their sides. The lumbar (lower back) region of the vertebral column has five vertebrae (L1–L5). The lumbar vertebrae are the largest of the vertebrae.

superior view

Thoracic Vertebra

lateral view

14. _____

15. _____

16. _____

17. _____

18. _____

19. _____

20. _____

21. _____

22. _____

superior view

Lumbar Vertebra

lateral view

23. _____

24. _____

25. _____

26. _____

27. _____

28. _____

29. _____

30. _____

31. _____

32. _____

Answers

1. Body, 2. Transverse foramen, 3. Pedicle, 4. Lamina, 5. Spinous process, 6. Vertebral foramen, 7. Superior articular process (facet), 8. Posterior tubercle, 9. Anterior tubercle, 10. Inferior articular process (facet), 11. Sulcus for ventral ramus of spinal nerve, 12. Body, 13. Superior articular facet, 14. Transverse foramen, 15. Spinous process, 16. Lamina, 17. Transverse costal facet, 18. Superior articular process (facet), 19. Superior costal demifacet, 20. Body, 21. Inferior costal demifacet, 22. Inferior articular process (facet), 23. Superior articular process (facet), 24. Lamina, 25. Spinous process, 26. Transverse process, 27. Mammillary process, 28. Pedicle, 29. Vertebral foramen, 30. Body, 31. Inferior articular process (facet), 32. Pedicle

The intervertebral discs are flexible cartilaginous structures that lie between adjacent vertebrae. Each disc has two parts: a central mass (the nucleus pulposus) and a surrounding fibrous layer (the annulus fibrosus). The thickness and shape of the discs vary in different parts of the vertebral column – they are relatively thin and flat in the thoracic region, thicker in the cervical region, and wedge-shaped in the lumbar region. The sacrum lies at the lower end of the spine beneath the lumbar vertebrae and forms part of the bony pelvis. A single curved bone in the adult, the sacrum develops from five separate vertebrae (S1–S5), which fuse to each other during early development to form a single bone. The coccyx, or tail bone, lies at the base of the spine. It is formed by the fusion of four vertebrae – a process that is usually complete by the time a person reaches their late twenties.

1. _____

5. _____

4. _____

Intervertebral Discs

2. _____

3. _____

6. _____

7. _____

8. _____

9. _____

Sacrum and Coccyx – anterior view

13. _____

12. _____

10. _____

11. _____

Sacrum and Coccyx – posterior view

Answers

Ribcage and Clavicle

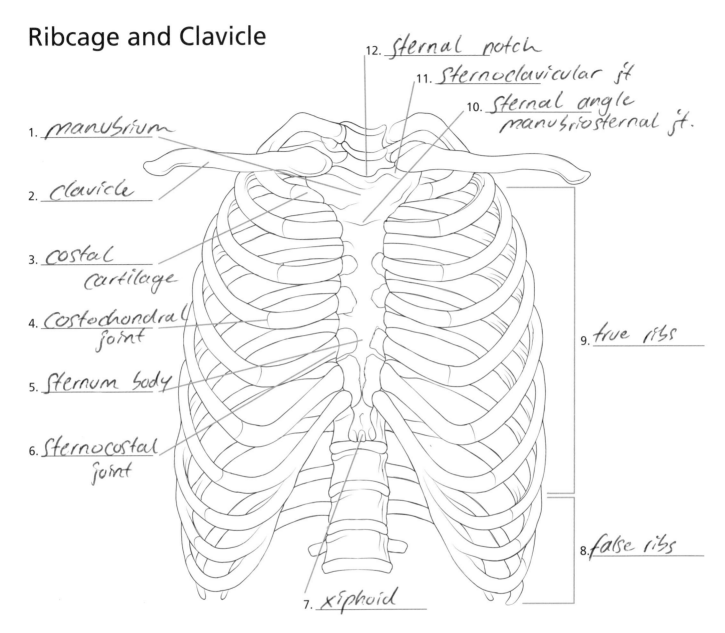

1. manubrium
2. clavicle
3. costal cartilage
4. costochondral joint
5. Sternum body
6. Sternocostal joint
7. xiphoid
8. false ribs
9. true ribs
10. sternal angle / manubriosternal jt.
11. Sternoclavicular jt
12. sternal notch

Ribcage – anterior view

There are twelve pairs of ribs. Pairs 1–7 are known as 'true ribs', and these ribs span around from the thoracic vertebrae at the back to the front, where they are joined to the sternum by costal cartilages. Pairs 8–10 are known as 'false ribs', and they span around from the vertebrae at the back but do not meet up with the sternum independently; rather, they are joined by their costal cartilages to the seventh rib. Pairs 11–12 are known as 'floating ribs' because they do not attach to the costal cartilage. These two pairs of ribs do not extend fully around to the front of the chest. The clavicles are a pair of short horizontal bones above the ribcage and are attached to the sternum and to the two scapulas on either side.

Answers

1. Manubrium, 2. Clavicle, 3. Costal cartilage, 4. Costochondral joint, 5. Body of sternum, 6. Sternocostal joint, 7. Xiphoid process, 8. False ribs (pairs 8–10), 9. True ribs (pairs 1–7), 10. Sternal angle, 11. Sternoclavicular joint, 12. Suprasternal notch

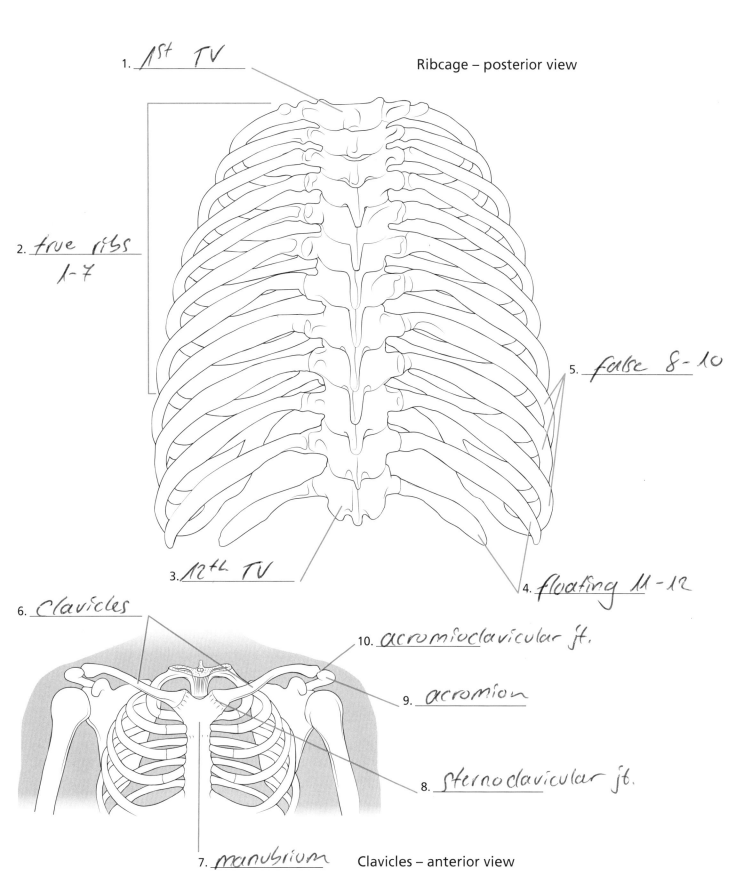

1. _1st TV_   Ribcage – posterior view

2. _true ribs 1-7_

5. _false 8-10_

3. _12th TV_

4. _floating 11-12_

6. _Clavicles_

10. _acromioclavicular jt._

9. _acromion_

8. _sternoclavicular jt._

7. _manubrium_   Clavicles – anterior view

Answers

1. First thoracic vertebra (T1), 2. True ribs (pairs 1–7), 3. Lowest thoracic vertebra (T12), 4. Floating ribs (pairs 11–12), 5. False ribs (pairs 8–10), 6. Clavicles, 7. Manubrium (of sternum), 8. Sternoclavicular joint, 9. Acromion (of scapula), 10. Acromioclavicular joint

Bones of the Upper Limb

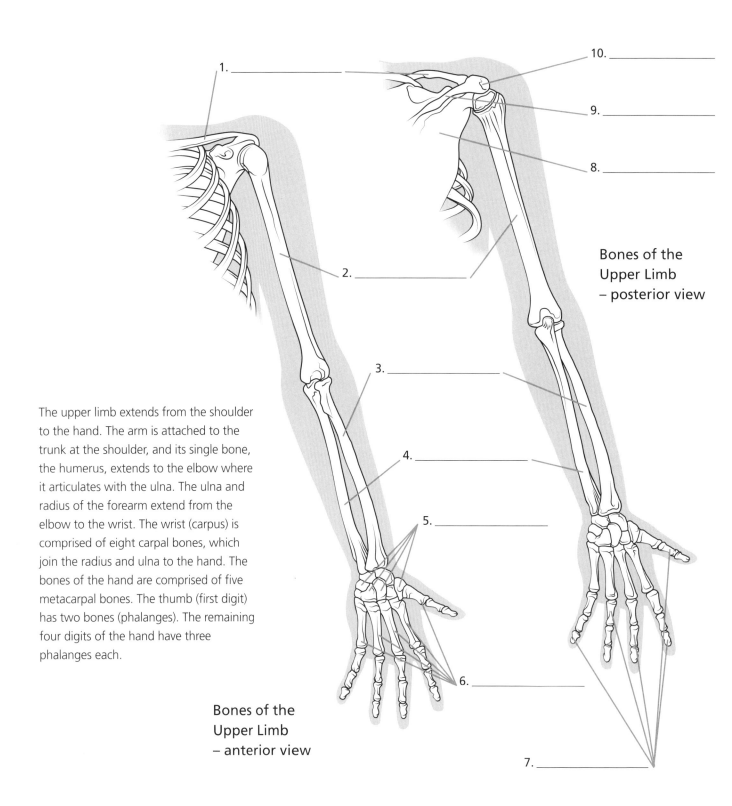

1. _____

10. _____

9. _____

8. _____

2. _____

Bones of the Upper Limb – posterior view

3. _____

4. _____

5. _____

6. _____

7. _____

The upper limb extends from the shoulder to the hand. The arm is attached to the trunk at the shoulder, and its single bone, the humerus, extends to the elbow where it articulates with the ulna. The ulna and radius of the forearm extend from the elbow to the wrist. The wrist (carpus) is comprised of eight carpal bones, which join the radius and ulna to the hand. The bones of the hand are comprised of five metacarpal bones. The thumb (first digit) has two bones (phalanges). The remaining four digits of the hand have three phalanges each.

Bones of the Upper Limb – anterior view

Answers
1. Clavicle, 2. Humerus, 3. Radius, 4. Ulna, 5. Carpal bones, 6. Metacarpal bones, 7. Phalanges, 8. Scapula, 9. Spine of scapula, 10. Acromion

The humerus of the arm and the scapula are the two major components of the shoulder joint, with the clavicle providing stability to the joint. The clavicle and scapula form the pectoral girdle, responsible for the attachment of the upper limb to the trunk. The clavicle acts as a strut to hold the upper limb away from the centre of the body. The scapula is a flat triangle-shaped bone that covers part of the upper back. Together, the scapula and humerus form the highly mobile shoulder joint. A multiaxial ball-and-socket joint, the shoulder joint is capable of movement in almost any direction.

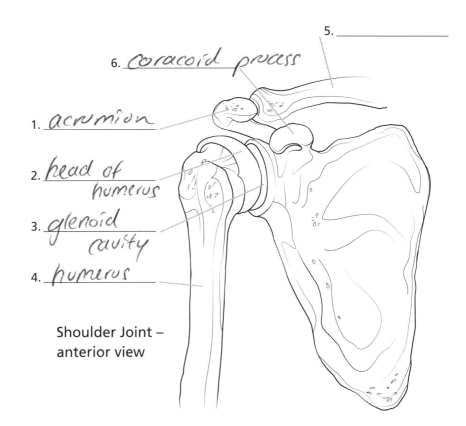

6. coracoid process
1. acromion
2. head of humerus
3. glenoid cavity
4. humerus
5. _____

Shoulder Joint – anterior view

16. _____
15. _____
14. _____
13. _____
12. _____
11. _____
7. _____
8. Spine of scapula
9. medial border
10. lateral border

Shoulder Joint – posterior view

Answers

1. Acromion, 2. Head of humerus, 3. Glenoid cavity, 4. Humerus, 5. Clavicle, 6. Coracoid process, 7. Clavicle, 8. Spine of scapula, 9. Medial border, 10. Lateral border, 11. Humerus, 12. Head of humerus, 13. Glenoid fossa, 14. Acromion, 15. Acromioclavicular joint, 16. Coracoid process

Bones of the Upper Limb

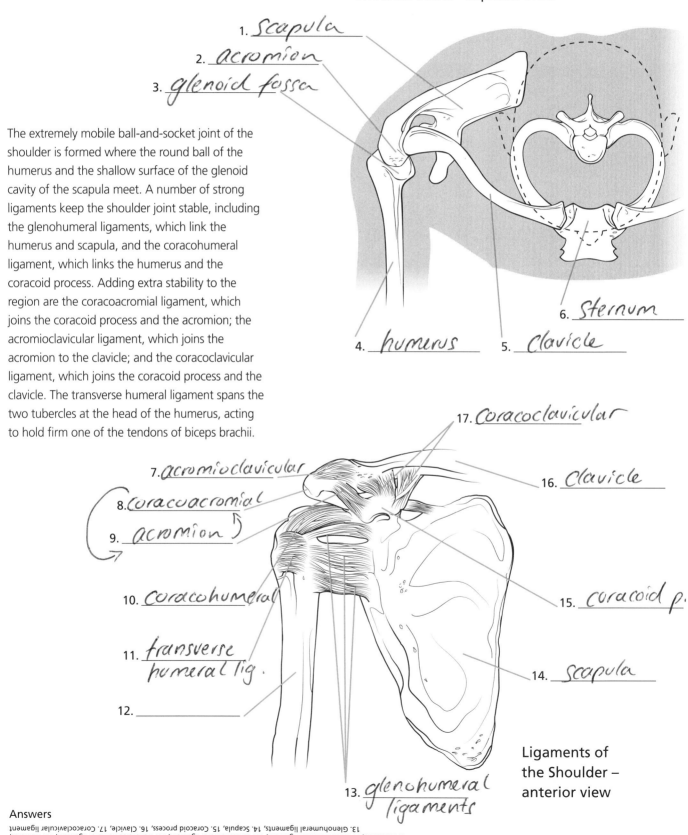

Shoulder Joint – superior view

1. Scapula
2. acromion
3. glenoid fossa

The extremely mobile ball-and-socket joint of the shoulder is formed where the round ball of the humerus and the shallow surface of the glenoid cavity of the scapula meet. A number of strong ligaments keep the shoulder joint stable, including the glenohumeral ligaments, which link the humerus and scapula, and the coracohumeral ligament, which links the humerus and the coracoid process. Adding extra stability to the region are the coracoacromial ligament, which joins the coracoid process and the acromion; the acromioclavicular ligament, which joins the acromion to the clavicle; and the coracoclavicular ligament, which joins the coracoid process and the clavicle. The transverse humeral ligament spans the two tubercles at the head of the humerus, acting to hold firm one of the tendons of biceps brachii.

6. Sternum
4. humerus
5. Clavicle

17. Coracoclavicular
16. Clavicle
7. acromioclavicular
8. coracoacromial
9. acromion
10. coracohumeral
11. transverse humeral lig.
12. _____
15. coracoid p.
14. scapula
13. glenohumeral ligaments

Ligaments of the Shoulder – anterior view

The humerus of the arm consists of a long cylindrical shaft with a rounded head at its proximal end, which articulates with the scapula at its glenoid fossa to form the shoulder joint, and with paired condyles at its distal end, which articulate with the radius and ulna to form the elbow joint. Other landmarks of the humerus include the deltoid tuberosity, the medial and lateral epicondyles, and the trochlea.

1. grt. tubercle
2. humeral head
3. anatomical n.
4. lesser tubercle
5. Intertubercular groove
6. surgical n.

7. deltoid tuberosity
8. radial groove

Humerus – anterior view

Humerus – posterior view

lateral
19. supra condylar ridges
18. medial
17. olecranon f.
16. coronoid fossa
15. medial condyle
14. m. epicondyle
13. trochlea

9. _____
10. radial fossa
11. lateral epic.
12. capitulum

Answers

Bones of the Upper Limb

The elbow is the joint between the expanded distal end of the humerus of the arm and the proximal ends of the ulna and radius of the forearm. It is a hinge joint, allowing flexion (bending) and extension (straightening). The principal flexion–extension action occurs between the distal end of the humerus and the proximal end of the ulna. The articulation between the radius and ulna forms a pivot joint, which allows rotational movement of the radius around the ulna. The bones of the elbow joint (humerus, radius, and ulna) are held together by strong fibrous ligaments. Joining the humerus to the ulna and olecranon, on the medial (inner) side of the joint, is the ulnar collateral ligament. On the lateral side of the joint, the radial collateral ligament joins the humerus to the radius, affixing to the radius at the annular ligament, which joins the head of the radius to the ulna.

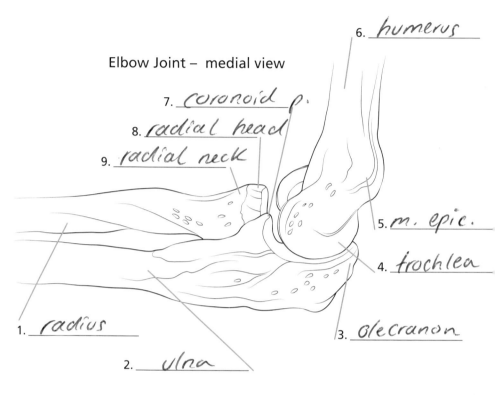

Elbow Joint – medial view

6. _humerus_

7. _coronoid p._
8. _radial head_
9. _radial neck_

5. _m. epic._

4. _trochlea_

1. _radius_

3. _olecranon_

2. _ulna_

16. _humerus_

Ligaments of the Elbow – medial view

10. _radius_

11. _oblique cord_

12. _ulna_

13. _annular ligament_

14. _ulnar collateral lig._

15. _olecranon_

Answers

1. Radius, 2. Ulna, 3. Olecranon, 4. Trochlea of humerus, 5. Medial epicondyle of humerus, 6. Humerus, 7. Coronoid process of ulna, 8. Head of radius, 9. Neck of radius, 10. Radius, 11. Oblique cord, 12. Ulna, 13. Annular ligament of radius, 14. Ulnar collateral ligament, 15. Olecranon, 16. Humerus

The radius is one of the two bones of the forearm. It is located on the thumb side, lying parallel to and rotating around the ulna. Near the uppermost end of the radius is a raised and roughened area called the radial tuberosity. At its larger distal end, the radius forms part of the wrist. The ulna lies on the medial side of the forearm, extending from the elbow to the wrist. The ulna is a long bone of irregular cross section, thickest at the proximal end and tapering towards the distal end. It projects above and behind the elbow.

Radius and Ulna – posterior view

1. *Olecranon*
2. *trochlear notch*
3. *proximal r/u*
4. *Coronoid p.*
5. *radial notch*
6. *radial head*
7. *radial neck*
8. *Ulnar tuberosity*
9. *radial tuberosity*
10. *Ulna*
11. *radius*

Radius and Ulna – anterior view

12. *distal r/u*
13. *Ulna head*
14. *Styloid p. Ulna*
15. *Styloid p. radius*

Bones of the Wrist and Hand

The wrist (carpus) is made up of eight carpal bones, which join the radius and ulna to the hand. The hand consists of the palm, the dorsum, and the thumb and fingers. Between the carpal bones of the wrist and the bones of the fingers (phalanges) are five metacarpal bones. Each of the four fingers (digits 2–5) contains three bones (the proximal, middle, and distal phalanges), whereas the thumb (digit 1) has two bones (the proximal and distal phalanges). The metacarpal bones join the phalanges at the metacarpophalangeal (MCP) joints.

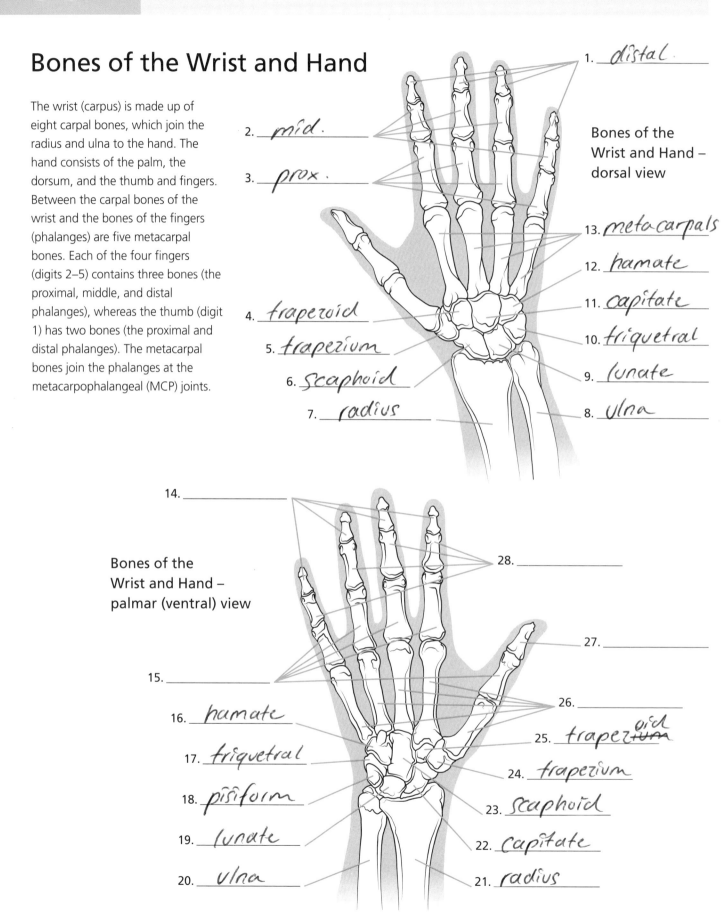

1. _distal_
2. _mid._
3. _prox._

Bones of the Wrist and Hand – dorsal view

4. _trapezoid_
5. _trapezium_
6. _scaphoid_
7. _radius_

13. _metacarpals_
12. _hamate_
11. _capitate_
10. _triquetral_
9. _lunate_
8. _ulna_

Bones of the Wrist and Hand – palmar (ventral) view

14. _____
15. _____
16. _hamate_
17. _triquetral_
18. _pisiform_
19. _lunate_
20. _ulna_

28. _____
27. _____
26. _____
25. _trapezoid_
24. _trapezium_
23. _scaphoid_
22. _capitate_
21. _radius_

Answers

Ligaments of the Wrist and Hand – palmar view

1. _____

2. _____

3. _____

4. _____

5. _____

6. _____

7. _____

8. _____

9. _____

10. _____

11. _____

12. _____

13. _____

The joints of the wrist are enclosed by a fibrous joint capsule and bound together by many ligaments. The radial and ulna collateral ligaments are rounded cords that attach the radius and ulnar to proximal (upper) carpal bones. There are also broad ligaments attaching the radius to proximal carpal bones: the palmar (or anterior) radiocarpal ligament (on the palm of the hand) and the dorsal (or posterior) radiocarpal ligament (on the back of the hand). The transverse carpal ligament (also called the flexor retinaculum) spans the carpal bones, and inside the joint capsule the intercarpal ligaments (dorsal and palmar) connect the individual carpal bones. The carpometacarpal ligaments (dorsal and palmar) join the distal (lower) carpal bones to the bases of the metacarpal bones of the hand. There are collateral ligaments between each metacarpal head and proximal phalanx (the upper digit).

Finger – medial view

14. _____
15. _____
16. _____
17. _____
18. _____
19. _____
20. _____
21. _____
22. _____
23. _____
24. _____
25. _____

Answers

Bones of the Pelvis

The bony pelvis is composed of the hip bones, sacrum, and coccyx. Each hip bone is made up of three bones (the ilium, ischium, and pubis). Each hip bone unites in front at the pubic symphysis and joins the sacrum behind at the sacroiliac joints. The male pelvis typically has a smaller heart-shaped inlet, a smaller pelvic outlet, and a more cone-shaped, longer cavity than the female pelvis. In addition, the male pelvis is typically distinguished by its larger bones, more defined muscle markings, and larger joint surfaces. Generally, the female pelvis has a larger pelvic inlet and outlet than the male pelvis. In addition, the length of the pelvic canal is shorter in the female pelvis, and its walls are more parallel than those of the male. The typical 'gynecoid' pelvic inlet is wider than it is deep, though the outlet is deeper than it is wide.

17. _____

16. Sacroiliac Jt.

15. Ilium _____

14. _____

1. Iliac crest

2. ASIS

3. AIIS

4. _____

Bones of the Pelvis (male) – anterior view

13. _____

12. _____

11. Obturator foramen

10. _____

5. _____

6. _____

9. _____

7. _____

8. pubic symphisys

Answers

1. Iliac crest, 2. Anterior superior iliac spine, 3. Anterior inferior iliac spine, 4. Superior ramus of pubis, 5. Pectineal line, 6. Ischium, 7. Pubic tubercle, 8. Pubic symphysis, 9. Inferior pubic ramus, 10. Coccyx, 11. Obturator foramen, 12. Iliopectineal eminence, 13. Sacrum, 14. Alar part of sacrum, 15. Ilium, 16. Sacroiliac joint, 17. Sacral promontory

The birth canal

The human birth canal passes through the ring made by the pubis, ilium, and sacrum. There is a very tight fit between the size of the baby's head (up to 8.5 cm wide) and the average internal diameter of the female pelvis (about 12.5 cm). Other internal organs (i.e. the rectum and urinary bladder) must be accommodated around the fetal head and uterine cervix. This makes human vaginal birth very difficult compared to that of other primates. If any condition increases the size of the baby (e.g. fetal hydrocephalus or maternal diabetes mellitus), or the woman has a very small pelvis, vaginal delivery may be impossible.

13. _____

12. _____

14. _____

11. _____

10. _____

1. _____

2. _____

3. _____

4. _____

5. _____

6. _____

7. _____

8. _____

9. _____

Bones of the Pelvis (female) – anterior view

Answers

Bones of the Pelvis

There are many ligaments in the pelvis, which connect and strengthen the articulations between the sacrum, coccyx, ilium, and pubic bones. Connecting the tuberosities of the sacrum and the ilium is the interosseous sacroiliac ligament. Also between the sacrum and ilium are the anterior sacroilial ligament and the two posterior sacroilial ligaments – short (upper) and long (lower). Between the sacrum and coccyx are the sacrococcygeal ligaments (anterior, posterior, and lateral). Between the sacrum and ischium are the sacrotuberous ligament, which connects the ischial tuberosity of the ischium to the sacrum and coccyx; and the sacrospinous ligament, which connects the ischial spine to the sacrum and coccyx. There is also the iliolumbar ligament, which connects the iliac crest to the L4 and L5 vertebrae. Connecting the two pubic bones are the anterior, posterior, superior, and arcuate ligaments.

Ligaments of the Pelvis and Hip – anterior view

9. *ant. longitudinal lig.*

1. _____

2. _____

3. _____

4. _____

5. _____

6. _____

7. _____

8. _____

Dislocation of the hip joint

The hip joint is very stable mechanically because of the close conformation between the femoral head and acetabulum, but also because of the strong ligaments that encircle the rim of the acetabulum. Dislocation of the hip joint is therefore usually due to powerful forces, such as those that occur during motor vehicle accidents. A major cause of hip dislocation is the patient's knees being forced against the car dashboard during sudden and powerful deceleration of the vehicle. The femoral head can be forced posteriorly out of the acetabulum, rupturing the ligaments. Surgical reduction of the dislocation is required.

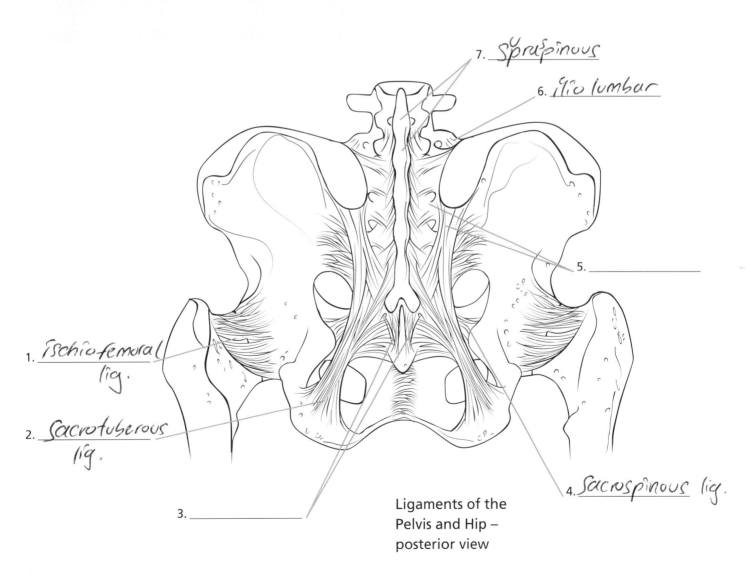

7. _Supraspinous_

6. _Ilio lumbar_

5. _____

1. _Ischiofemoral lig._

2. _Sacrotuberous lig._

4. _Sacrospinous lig._

3. _____

Ligaments of the
Pelvis and Hip –
posterior view

Answers

Bones of the Lower Limb

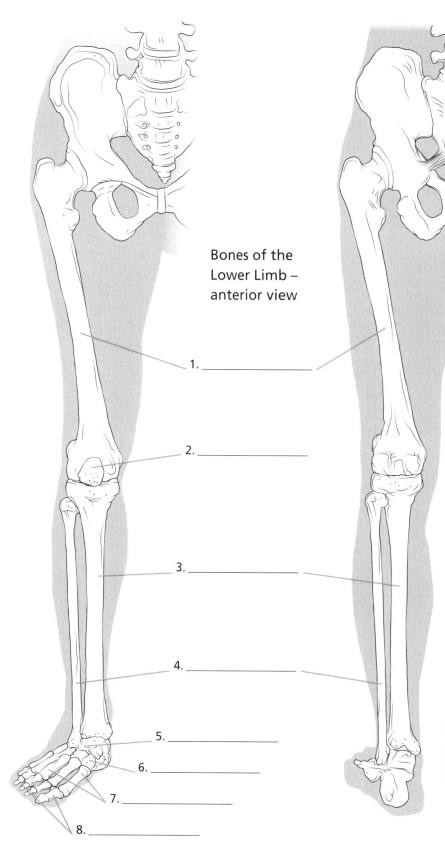

Bones of the
Lower Limb –
anterior view

1. _____

2. _____

3. _____

4. _____

5. _____

6. _____

7. _____

8. _____

The bones of the lower limb include the femur in the thigh, and the tibia and fibula in the leg. The femur is the longest bone in the body. The femur articulates with the kneecap (patella), a bone within the tendon of the quadriceps femoris muscle. The tibia is the second-longest bone in the body. The tibia and fibula together form the bones of the leg. The fibula is thin and bears little weight. The tibia and fibula articulate with the talus bone at the ankle joint. The bones of the foot are the tarsals, metatarsals, and phalanges.

Bones of the
Lower Limb –
posterior view

Answers

1. Femur, 2. Patella, 3. Tibia, 4. Fibula, 5. Talus, 6. Tarsal bones, 7. Metatarsal bones, 8. Phalanges

Extending from the hip to the knee, the femur (thigh bone) is the longest and strongest bone in the body. Features of the femur include a rounded head, a long neck with two enlargements (the greater trochanter and the lesser trochanter), and two protuberances at the distal end of the femur (the lateral condyle and the medial condyle).

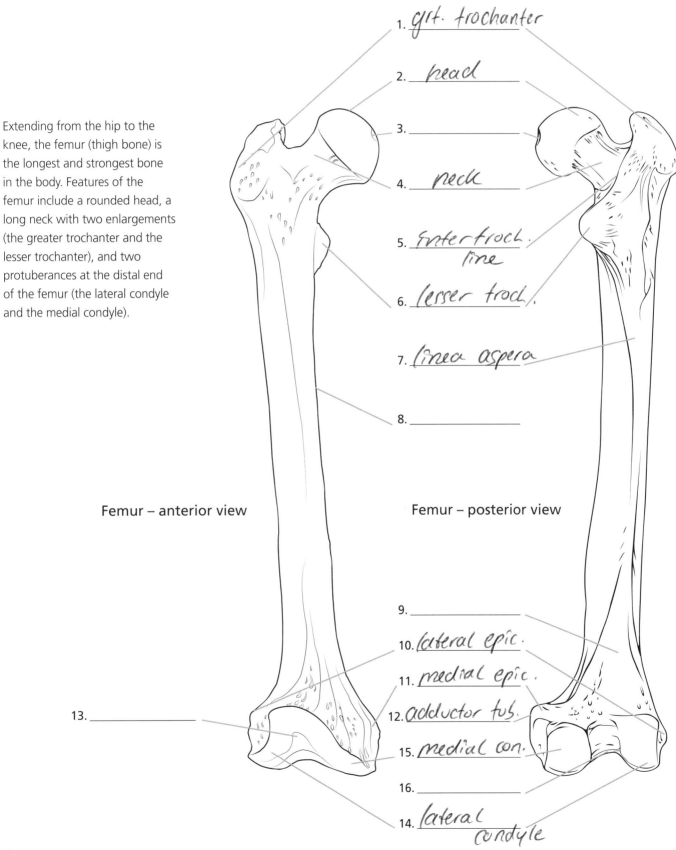

Femur – anterior view

Femur – posterior view

1. grt. trochanter
2. head
3. _____
4. neck
5. Inter troch. line
6. lesser troch.
7. linea aspera
8. _____
9. _____
10. lateral epic.
11. medial epic.
12. adductor tub.
13. _____
14. lateral condyle
15. medial con.
16. _____

Bones of the Lower Limb

Ligaments play an important role in strengthening the knee joint. The medial side is reinforced by the tibial (medial) collateral ligament. The lateral side is reinforced by the fibular (lateral) collateral ligament. The two cruciate ligaments are internal to the joint capsule. The knee joint is a complex hinge joint between the femur, tibia, and patella. The lower end of the femur has a concave surface at the front, into which the back of the patella fits, and two rounded condyles at its base. The upper surface of the tibia is relatively flat. Depth to the tibial plateaus is provided by the medial and lateral menisci, which are wedge-shaped fibrocartilages. Each of the rounded condyles of the femur fits into the shallow sockets formed by the corresponding tibial plateau bounded by the menisci. The articulating surfaces are lined with hyaline cartilage.

Bones and Ligaments of the Knee – anterior view

1. _femur_
2. _PCL_
3. _lat. condyle_
4. _LCL_
5. _lateral meniscus_
6. _ACL (LAMP)_
12. _m. condyle_
11. _med. meniscus_
10. _MCL_
9. _patellar lig._
8. _tibia_
7. _patella_

Bones of the Knee – lateral view

13. _femur_
14. _patella_
15. _lat. condyle_
16. _tibia_
19. _articular cartilage_
18. _tibial plateau_
17. _fibula_

The tibia (commonly known as the shin bone) is the innermost bone of the leg and the thicker of the two bones. The second longest bone in the body, the tibia features a broad head and a cylindrical shaft that widens at the lower end to include the medial malleolus. The medial malleolus of the tibia is the small protruding bump on the inside of the ankle. The fibula is the long slender bone on the outside of the leg, extending from just below the knee to the ankle, where its lower end forms the outer side of the ankle joint.

1. *lat. condyle*
2. *Entercondylar* — *eminence*
3. *med. condyle*
4. *fibula head*
5. *fibula neck*
6. *tibial tuberosity*
7. _____
8. *tibia*
9. *fibula*
10. *fibular notch*
11. *med. malleolus*
12. *Enferior artic. surface*
13. *lat. malleolus*

Tibia and Fibula –
anterior view

Tibia and Fibula –
posterior view

Answers

1. Lateral tibial condyle, 2. Intercondylar eminence, 3. Medial tibial condyle, 4. Head of fibula, 5. Neck of fibula, 6. Tibial tuberosity, 7. Anterior border, 8. Tibia, 9. Fibula, 10. Fibular notch, 11. Medial malleolus, 12. Inferior articular surface, 13. Lateral malleolus

Bones of the Ankle and Foot

1. calcaneus

5. talus
4. navicular
3. cuboid
2. cuneiforms

Bones of the Ankle – medial view

10. talus
9. navicular
8. cuboid
7. ~~calcaneus~~ calcaneus
6. cuneiforms

Bones of the Ankle – lateral view

The ankle attaches the tibia and fibula of the leg to the talus of the foot. Prominent features of the ankle joint include the medial malleolus on the tibia and the lateral malleolus on the fibula. The two malleoli, together with part of the tibia, form a socket in which the talus can move. The bones of the foot are the tarsals (seven bones in total: the talus, calcaneus, navicular, cuboid, and the three cuneiform bones [lateral, intermediate, and medial]); the five metatarsals; and the fourteen phalanges of the toes. The tarsus (the back half of the foot) is formed by the seven irregularly shaped tarsal bones.

11. _____
12. _____
13. _____
14. _____
15. calcaneus

22. _____
21. _____
20. _____
19. _____
18. _____
17. _____
16. talus

Bones and Ligaments of the Ankle – posterior view

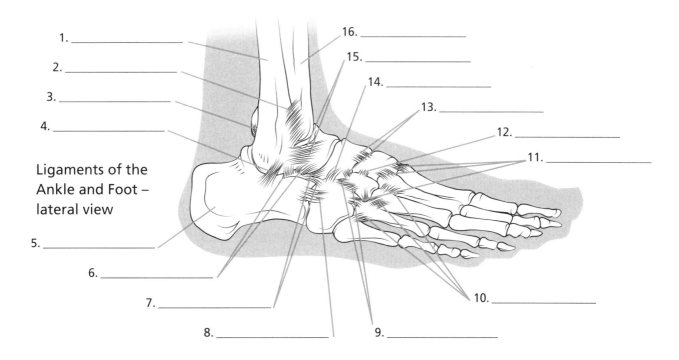

1. _____

2. _____

3. _____

4. _____

Ligaments of the Ankle and Foot – lateral view

5. _____

6. _____

7. _____

8. _____

16. _____

15. _____

14. _____

13. _____

12. _____

11. _____

10. _____

9. _____

Numerous ligaments make the ankle joint strong and stable. On the lateral side of the joint, three cord-like ligaments (the anterior talofibular ligament, the posterior talofibular ligament, and the calcaneofibular ligament) attach the lateral malleolus of the fibula to the talus and calcaneus. On the medial side of the joint, the broad, strong, triangular deltoid (medial) ligament connects the medial malleolus of the tibia to three of the tarsal bones (the talus, the navicular, and the calcaneus). Ligaments also strengthen the joints between each of the bones of the talus, and small ligaments attach the talus bones to adjoining metatarsal bones.

Ligaments of the Ankle and Foot – medial view

17. _____

18. _____

19. _____

20. _____

29. _____

28. _____

27. _____

26. _____

21. _____

22. _____

23. _____

24. _____

25. _____

Answers

1. Fibula, 2. Anterior tibiofibular ligament, 3. Posterior tibiofibular ligament, 4. Calcaneofibular ligament, 5. Calcaneus, 6. Talocalcaneal ligament, 7. Bifurcate ligament, 8. Dorsal calcaneocuboid ligament, 9. Dorsal cuneocuboid ligament, 10. Dorsal metatarsal ligaments, 11. Dorsal tarsometatarsal ligaments, 12. Dorsal cuneonavicular ligaments, 13. Dorsal intercuneiform ligament, 14. Dorsal cuboideonavicular ligament, 15. Anterior talofibular ligament, 16. Tibia, 17. Tibiocalcaneal part of medial deltoid ligament, 18. Anterior tibiotalar part of medial deltoid ligament, 19. Dorsal talonavicular ligament, 20. Dorsal tarsometatarsal ligaments, 21. Medial intercuneiform joint, 22. Dorsal cuneonavicular ligaments, 23. Tibionavicular part of medial deltoid ligament, 24. Short plantar ligament, 25. Long plantar ligament, 26. Plantar calcaneonavicular (spring) ligament, 27. Posterior talocalcaneal ligament, 28. Medial talocalcaneal ligament, 29. Posterior tibiotalar part of medial deltoid ligament

Body Movements

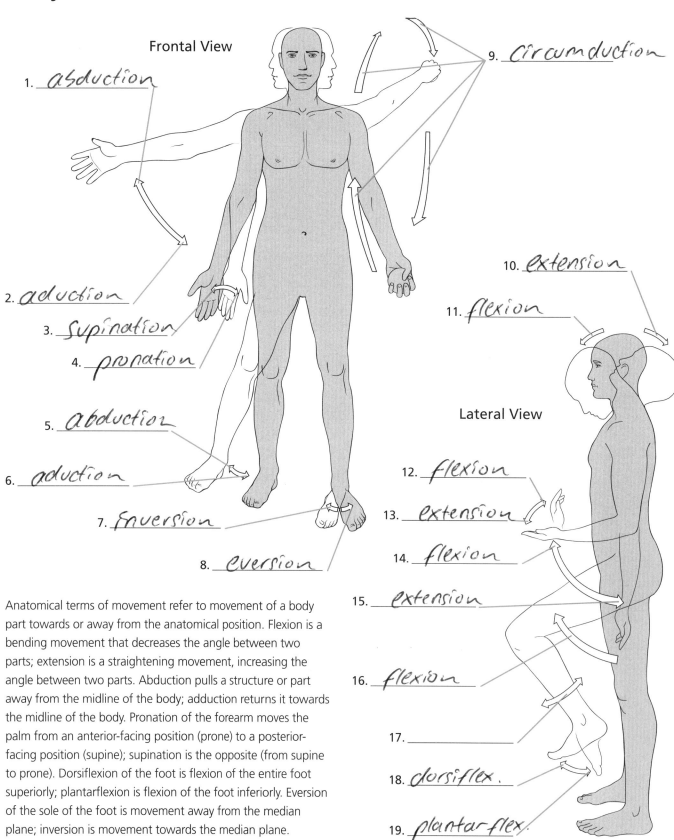

Frontal View

1. abduction
2. adduction
3. supination
4. pronation
5. abduction
6. adduction
7. inversion
8. eversion

9. circumduction
10. extension
11. flexion

Lateral View

12. flexion
13. extension
14. flexion
15. extension
16. flexion
17.
18. dorsiflex.
19. plantarflex.

Anatomical terms of movement refer to movement of a body part towards or away from the anatomical position. Flexion is a bending movement that decreases the angle between two parts; extension is a straightening movement, increasing the angle between two parts. Abduction pulls a structure or part away from the midline of the body; adduction returns it towards the midline of the body. Pronation of the forearm moves the palm from an anterior-facing position (prone) to a posterior-facing position (supine); supination is the opposite (from supine to prone). Dorsiflexion of the foot is flexion of the entire foot superiorly; plantarflexion is flexion of the foot inferiorly. Eversion of the sole of the foot is movement away from the median plane; inversion is movement towards the median plane.

Answers

1. Abduction, 2. Adduction, 3. Supination, 4. Pronation, 5. Abduction, 6. Adduction, 7. Inversion, 8. Eversion, 9. Circumduction, 10. Extension, 11. Flexion, 12. Wrist flexion, 13. Wrist extension, 14. Elbow flexion, 15. Elbow extension, 16. Flexion, 17. Medial and lateral rotation, 18. Dorsiflexion, 19. Plantarflexion

Joints

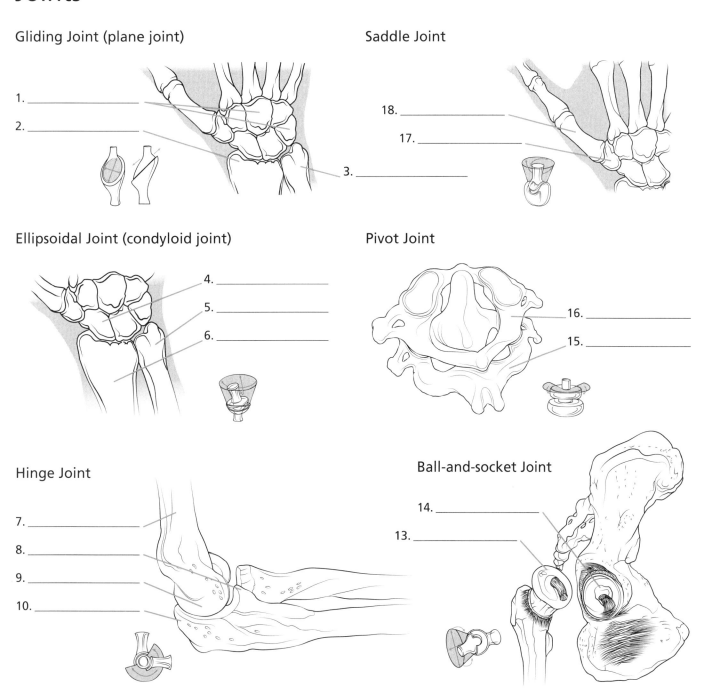

Gliding Joint (plane joint)

1. _____
2. _____
3. _____

Saddle Joint

18. _____
17. _____

Ellipsoidal Joint (condyloid joint)

4. _____
5. _____
6. _____

Pivot Joint

16. _____
15. _____

Hinge Joint

7. _____
8. _____
9. _____
10. _____

Ball-and-socket Joint

14. _____
13. _____

There are six types of synovial joints found in the appendicular skeleton: ball-and-socket, ellipsoidal (condyloid), gliding (plane), hinge, pivot, and saddle joints. Each permits a different range of movement, with the ball-and-socket joint being the most mobile. In a synovial joint, the ends of the bones are smooth and are covered by articular cartilage with an extremely low coefficient of friction. The two bones are bound together by a capsule of fibrous tissue. The fibrous capsule is lined on the inside with a synovial membrane that secretes synovial fluid to lubricate the joint and nourish the cartilage. The joint is reinforced by ligaments, which are made up of fibres of connective tissue.

Answers

1. Carpal bones, 2. Radius, 3. Ulna, 4. Ulna, 5. Scaphoid bone, 6. Radius, 7. Ulna, 8. Humerus, 7. Radius, 6. Ulna, 9. Coronoid process of ulna, 10. Olecranon, 11. Ulna, 12. Radius, 13. Head of femur (ball), 14. Acetabular fossa (socket), 15. Axis, 16. Atlas, 17. Trapezium bone, 18. Metacarpal bone of thumb

Joints

1. _____

2. _____

Shoulder Joint

3. _____

4. _____

5. _____

6. _____

Movement
of the Shoulder
(humeroscapular joint)

The shoulder joint is a multiaxial ball-and-socket joint between the humerus and the scapula, allowing movement in almost any direction. The humerus can be flexed, extended, abducted, adducted, and rotated around its axis. The temporomandibular joint is the joint between the mandible and the skull. This joint allows gliding (backwards, forwards, and sideways) movements as well as a hinge movement. The elbow is the joint between the humerus and the radius and ulna. The ulna articulates with the humerus, forming a hinge joint, which allows flexion and extension. The articulation between the radius and ulna forms a pivot joint, which allows rotational movement. The knee is a complex bicondylar joint between the femur, tibia, and patella, and its main movements are flexion and extension, although some backwards and forwards gliding movement and some rotation also occur. The hip is an extremely stable and strong ball-and-socket joint between the femur and the hip bone. The hip's capability of rotation is second only to that of the shoulder joint.

Temporomandibular Joint

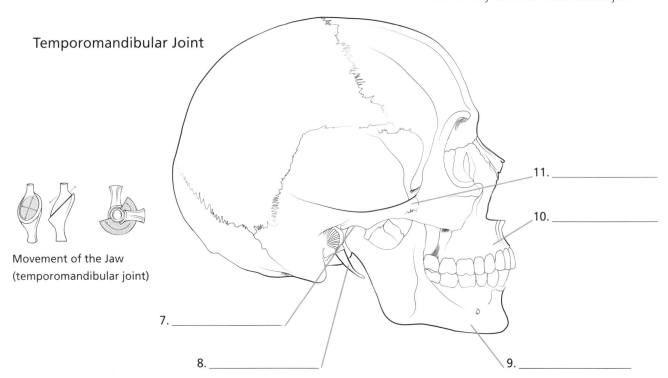

Movement of the Jaw
(temporomandibular joint)

7. _____

8. _____

9. _____

10. _____

11. _____

Answers

1. Coracoid process, 2. Acromion, 3. Head of humerus, 4. Glenoid cavity, 5. Humerus, 6. Clavicle, 7. Temporomandibular joint, 8. Styloid process, 9. Mandible, 10. Maxilla, 11. Zygomatic arch

1. _____

2. _____

3. _____

4. _____

5. _____

6. _____

Movement of the Elbow

9. _____

8. _____

7. _____

Elbow Joint

23. _____

Knee Joint

17. _____

18. _____

19. _____

10. _____

11. _____

Movement of the Knee
(tibiofemoral joint)

Hip Joint

20. _____

21. _____

12. _____

13. _____

14. _____

15. _____

22. _____

16. _____

Movement of the Hip
(acetabulofemoral joint)

Answers

Muscular System

Muscular System – anterior view

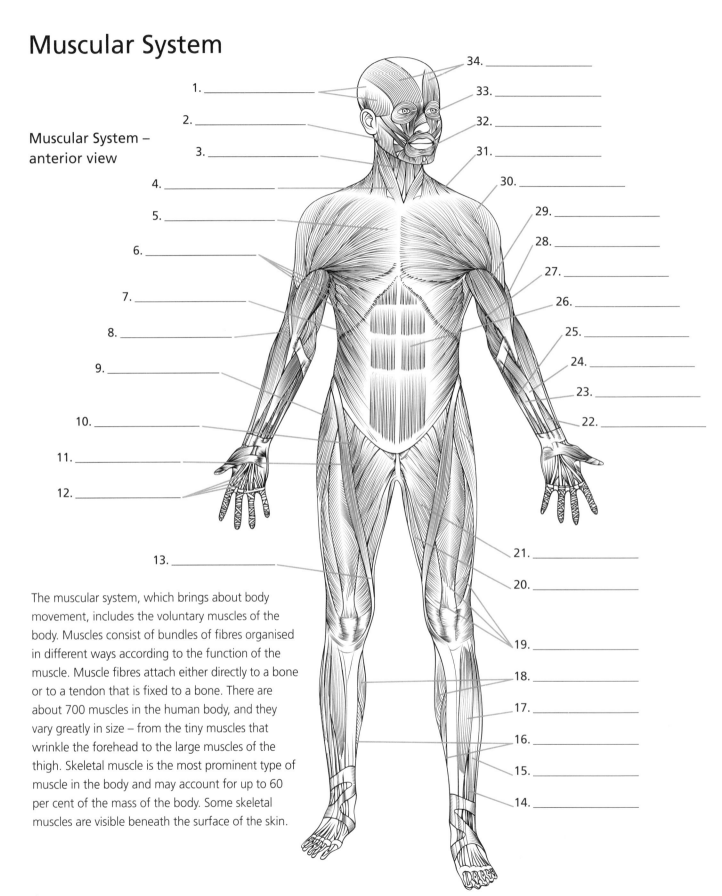

1. _____
2. _____
3. _____
4. _____
5. _____
6. _____
7. _____
8. _____
9. _____
10. _____
11. _____
12. _____
13. _____

34. _____
33. _____
32. _____
31. _____
30. _____
29. _____
28. _____
27. _____
26. _____
25. _____
24. _____
23. _____
22. _____
21. _____
20. _____
19. _____
18. _____
17. _____
16. _____
15. _____
14. _____

The muscular system, which brings about body movement, includes the voluntary muscles of the body. Muscles consist of bundles of fibres organised in different ways according to the function of the muscle. Muscle fibres attach either directly to a bone or to a tendon that is fixed to a bone. There are about 700 muscles in the human body, and they vary greatly in size – from the tiny muscles that wrinkle the forehead to the large muscles of the thigh. Skeletal muscle is the most prominent type of muscle in the body and may account for up to 60 per cent of the mass of the body. Some skeletal muscles are visible beneath the surface of the skin.

Answers

1. Temporalis, 2. Masseter, 3. Sternohyoid, 4. Sternocleidomastoid, 5. Pectoralis major, 6. Serratus anterior, 7. External oblique, 8. Brachioradialis, 9. Tensor fasciae latae, 10. Iliopsoas, 11. Pectineus, 12. Lumbricals, 13. Sartorius, 14. Extensor hallucis longus, 15. Extensor digitorum longus, 16. Soleus, 17. Tibialis anterior, 18. Gastrocnemius, 19. Quadriceps femoris, 20. Adductor magnus, 21. Adductor longus, 22. Flexor digitorum superficialis, 23. Palmaris longus, 24. Flexor carpi radialis, 25. Flexor carpi ulnaris, 26. Rectus abdominis, 27. Triceps brachii, 28. Brachialis, 29. Biceps brachii, 30. Deltoid, 31. Trapezius, 32. Orbicularis oris, 33. Orbicularis oculi, 34. Frontalis

Muscular System – posterior view

Muscular System – lateral view

42. _____

24. _____

23. _____

22. _____

41. _____

21. _____

20. _____

40. _____

39. _____

38. _____

37. _____

36. _____

19. _____

35. _____

18. _____

17. _____

16. _____

34. _____

33. _____

32. _____

15. _____

14. _____

31. _____

30. _____

29. _____

13. _____

28. _____

27. _____

12. _____

11. _____

26. _____

25. _____

Answers

Muscle Types

Muscle fibres are elongated cells containing myofibrils. Each myofibril is made up of thousands of overlapping thin actin filaments and thicker myosin filaments. Where they overlap, actin and myosin filaments are linked by connections (cross-bridges) that participate in muscle shortening (contraction). Muscles are classified based on their general shape – some muscles have mainly parallel fibres, and others have oblique fibres. In the case of circular muscles (sphincters), the fibres are arranged in concentric circles. In common spindle-shaped muscles, all muscle fibres run from one tendon to another. Pennate muscles have a feather-like appearance, and their fibres run obliquely down to the tendon. Some spiral muscles have the capacity to turn half a rotation between their attachments, while others twist around a bone. The shape and arrangement of muscle fibres reflect the function of the muscle.

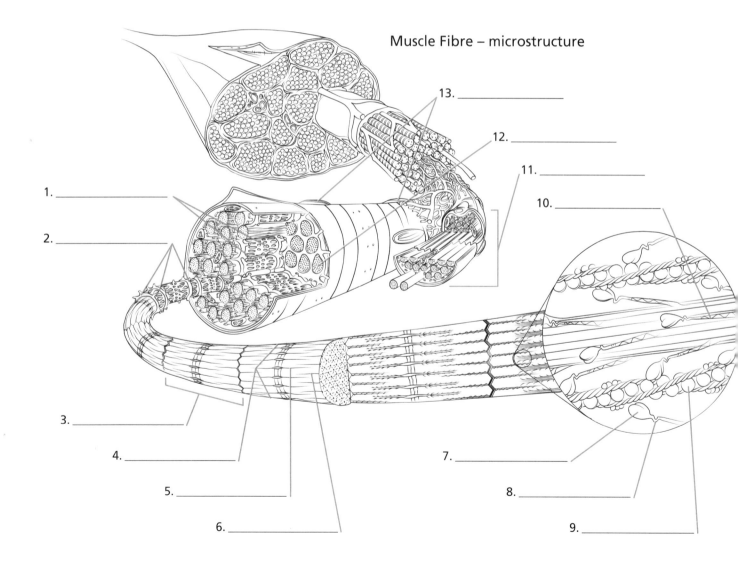

Muscle Fibre – microstructure

13. _____

12. _____

11. _____

10. _____

1. _____

2. _____

3. _____

4. _____

5. _____

6. _____

7. _____

8. _____

9. _____

Answers

1. Sarcoplasmic reticulum, 2. Transverse tubules, 3. Sarcomere, 4. Myofibril, 5. Myosin, 6. Actin, 7. Myosin head, 8. Myosin crossbridge, 9. Actin, 10. Myosin tail, 11. Muscle fibre, 12. Myofibril, 13. Nuclei

Muscle Shapes

1. _____

2. _____

3. _____

4. _____

5. _____

6. _____

7. _____

8. _____

9. _____

10. _____

11. _____

12. _____

13. _____

14. _____

15. _____

16. _____

Answers

1. Unipennate, 2. Bipennate, 3. Multipennate, 4. Spiral, 5. Radial, 6. Quadrate, 7. Strap, 8. Cruciate, 9. Triangular, 10. Multicaudal, 11. Digastric, 12. Circular, 13. Fusiform, 14. Bicipital, 15. Tricipital, 16. Quadricipital

Muscles of the Head and Neck

**Superficial and
Deep Muscles of
the Head and Neck –
anterior view**

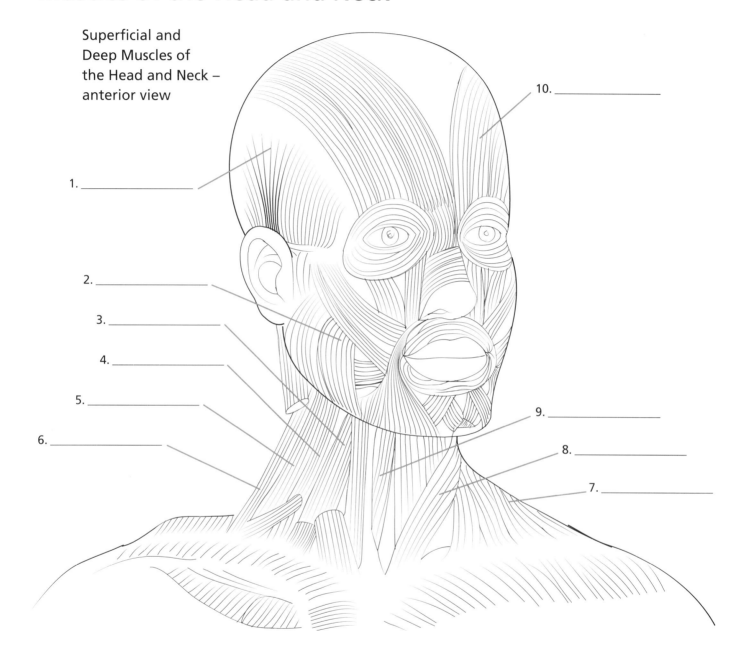

1. _____

2. _____

3. _____

4. _____

5. _____

6. _____

7. _____

8. _____

9. _____

10. _____

The muscles covering the scalp region are collectively known as the epicranial muscles, and include the occipitalis, frontalis, and temporoparietal muscles. The neck muscles attach to the front, back, and sides of the vertebrae, producing forwards, backwards, and sideways movements. Those with an oblique orientation also produce rotation (turning). The largest musculature lies to the back. Some of these muscles are exclusively related to moving the head and neck (for example, splenius capitis and cervicis, and semispinalis capitis and cervicis), while others are related to moving the shoulder (for example, trapezius, levator scapulae) or raising the upper two ribs (scalene muscles).

Answers

1. Temporalis, 2. Masseter, 3. Anterior scalene, 4. Middle scalene, 5. Levator scapulae, 6. Trapezius (cut), 7. Trapezius, 8. Sternocleidomastoid, 9. Sternohyoid, 10. Frontalis

Superficial Muscles of the Head and Neck – lateral view

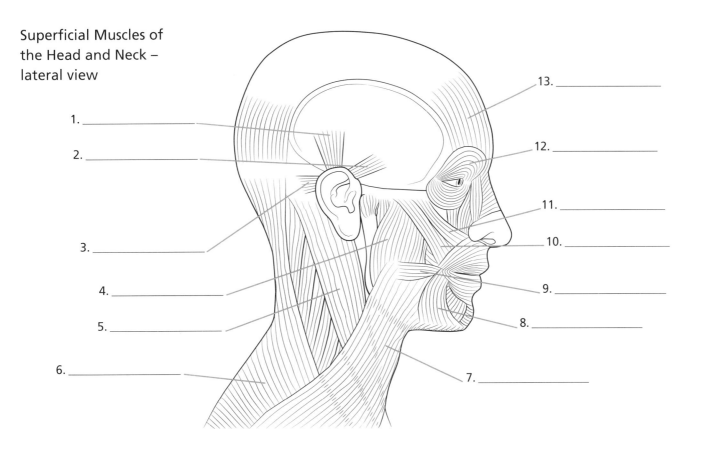

1. _____
2. _____
3. _____
4. _____
5. _____
6. _____
7. _____
8. _____
9. _____
10. _____
11. _____
12. _____
13. _____

Deep Muscles of the Head and Neck – lateral view

14. _____
15. _____
16. _____
17. _____
18. _____
19. _____
20. _____
21. _____
22. _____
23. _____
24. _____
25. _____
26. _____
27. _____
28. _____

Answers

1. Auricularis superior, 2. Auricularis anterior, 3. Auricularis posterior, 4. Masseter, 5. Sternocleidomastoid, 6. Trapezius, 7. Platysma, 8. Depressor anguli oris, 9. Risorius, 10. Zygomaticus major, 11. Zygomaticus minor, 12. Orbicularis oculi, 13. Frontalis, 14. Semispinalis capitis, 15. Splenius cervicis, 16. Levator scapulae, 17. Anterior scalene, 18. Middle scalene, 19. Posterior scalene, 20. Omohyoid (inferior belly), 21. Sternohyoid, 22. Omohyoid (superior belly), 23. Thyrohyoid, 24. Digastric (anterior belly), 25. Digastric (posterior belly), 26. Medial pterygoid, 27. Lateral pterygoid, 28. Temporalis

Muscles of the Head and Neck

Superficial Muscles
of the Jaw –
lateral view

The superficial muscles of the jaw (the temporalis and the masseter) in combination with the deep muscles (the medial pterygoid and the lateral pterygoid) are the muscles of mastication. Combined, they allow the jaw to move up, down, to the side, forwards, and backwards. The temporalis muscle arises at the temporal fossa and temporal fascia and inserts at the coronoid process of the mandible; the masseter arises at the inferior border of the zygomatic arch and inserts at the ramus and coronoid process of the mandible. The medial pterygoid (deep part) and lateral pterygoid (inferior head) arise at the lateral pterygoid plate; the medial pterygoid (superficial part) at the tuberosity of the maxilla; and the lateral pterygoid (superior head) at the infratemporal surface of the greater wing of the sphenoid bone and the pterygoid ridge. The medial pterygoid inserts at the medial surface of the mandibular ramus and the angle of the mandible; and the lateral pterygoid inserts at the temporomandibular joint and the neck of the mandible.

7. _____

6. _____

5. _____

1. _____

2. _____

3. _____

4. _____

13. _____

12. _____

Deep Muscles
of the Jaw –
lateral view

8. _____

9. _____

10. _____

11. _____

Answers

Muscles of Facial Expression – lateral view

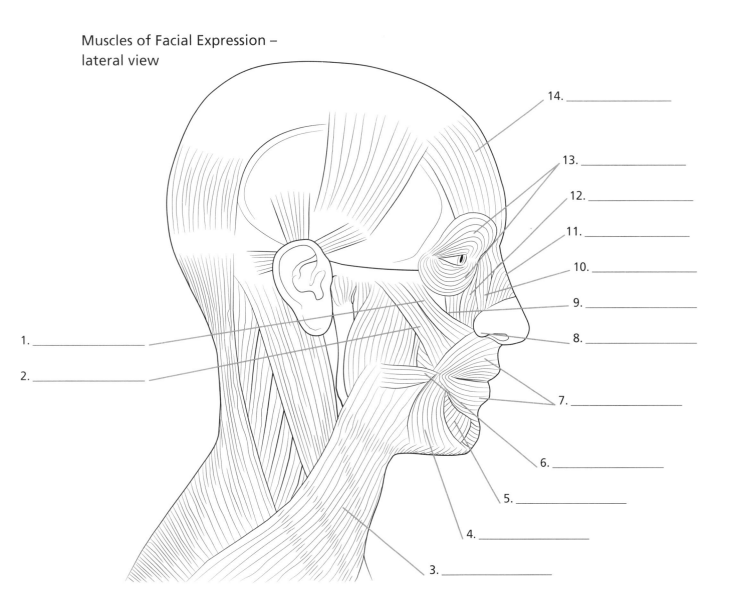

14. _____

13. _____

12. _____

11. _____

10. _____

9. _____

8. _____

7. _____

6. _____

5. _____

4. _____

3. _____

2. _____

1. _____

The muscles of the face are responsible for facial expression. There is a circular muscle around the mouth, and one around each eye. Other muscles spread out over the face from the edge of the circular muscles. The muscles of the eye region are the frontalis, orbicularis oculi, and procerus. The muscles found in the nasal region are the procerus, levator labii superioris alaeque nasi, and nasalis. The muscles of the mouth are the zygomaticus major, zygomaticus minor, levator labii superioris, levator labii superioris alaeque nasi, orbicularis oris, buccinator, depressor labii inferioris, and depressor anguli oris.

Answers

1. Zygomaticus minor, 2. Zygomaticus major, 3. Platysma, 4. Depressor anguli oris, 5. Depressor labii inferioris, 6. Buccinator, 7. Orbicularis oris, 8. Nasalis (compressor naris and depressor naris), 9. Levator labii superioris, 10. Levator labii superioris alaeque nasi, 11. Procerus, 12. Levator anguli oris, 13. Orbicularis oculi, 14. Frontalis

Muscles of the Head and Neck

The movement of the eyeball is controlled by six muscles (superior rectus, medial rectus, lateral rectus, inferior rectus, superior oblique, and inferior oblique). These muscles cause the eye to look up, down, left, and right. The levator palpebrae superioris is involved in movement of the upper eyelid. The trochlea is a hook of bone that acts as a fulcrum for the superior oblique muscle. The inferior rectus, medial rectus, superior rectus, lateral rectus, and levator palpebrae superioris muscles all arise at the dural sheath around the optic nerve; the superior oblique arises at the sphenoid bone; and the inferior oblique at the maxillary bone. The six ocular muscles insert on the sclera, and the levator palpebrae superioris at the tarsal plate of the upper eyelid.

Muscles of the Eye – superior view

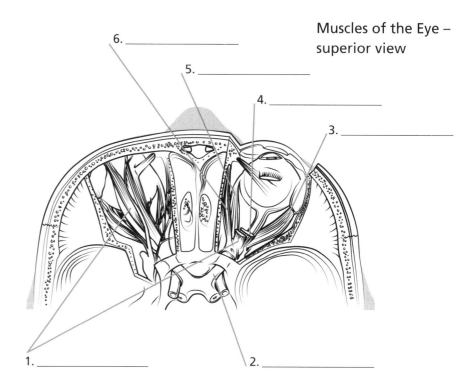

6. _____
5. _____
4. _____
3. _____
1. _____
2. _____

Muscles of the Eye – lateral view

7. _____
8. _____
9. _____
10. _____
11. _____
16. _____
15. _____
14. _____
13. _____
12. _____

1. _____
2. _____
3. _____
4. _____
5. _____
6. _____
7. _____
8. _____
9. _____
10. _____
11. _____
12. _____

Muscles of the Neck – transverse section

The transverse section of the neck shows the relationship among the components of the neck column. The neck can be divided into two major columns. At the back, the nuchal region includes the cervical vertebrae and their supporting musculature. In front, the neck includes a visceral column containing the larynx, trachea, pharynx, and oesophagus. The constrictor muscles of the pharynx are involved in the digestive process, being responsible for moving food down to the oesophagus. The stylopharyngeus and the deeper muscles, the palatopharyngeus and the salpingopharyngeus, are involved in elevating the larynx. The superior constrictor muscle arises at the pterygoid plate of the sphenoid bone; the middle constrictor at the horns of the hyoid bone; and the inferior constrictor at the cricoid and thyroid cartilages of the larynx. All three constrictor muscles insert at the median raphe of the pharynx. The stylopharyngeus arises at the styloid process; the salpingopharyngeus at the cartilage of the auditory tube; and the palatopharyngeus at the hard palate in the oral cavity. These three muscles insert at the thyroid cartilage of the larynx.

Muscles of the Pharynx – posterior view

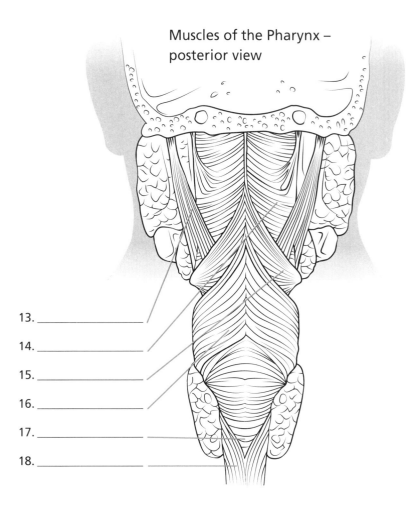

13. _____
14. _____
15. _____
16. _____
17. _____
18. _____

Muscles of the Back

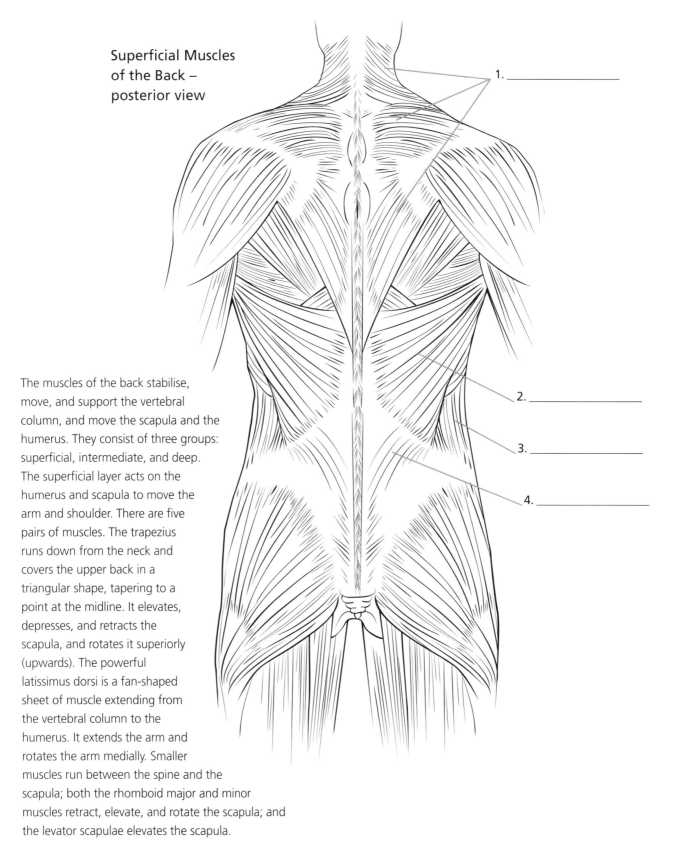

Superficial Muscles of the Back – posterior view

1. _____

2. _____

3. _____

4. _____

The muscles of the back stabilise, move, and support the vertebral column, and move the scapula and the humerus. They consist of three groups: superficial, intermediate, and deep. The superficial layer acts on the humerus and scapula to move the arm and shoulder. There are five pairs of muscles. The trapezius runs down from the neck and covers the upper back in a triangular shape, tapering to a point at the midline. It elevates, depresses, and retracts the scapula, and rotates it superiorly (upwards). The powerful latissimus dorsi is a fan-shaped sheet of muscle extending from the vertebral column to the humerus. It extends the arm and rotates the arm medially. Smaller muscles run between the spine and the scapula; both the rhomboid major and minor muscles retract, elevate, and rotate the scapula; and the levator scapulae elevates the scapula.

Answers

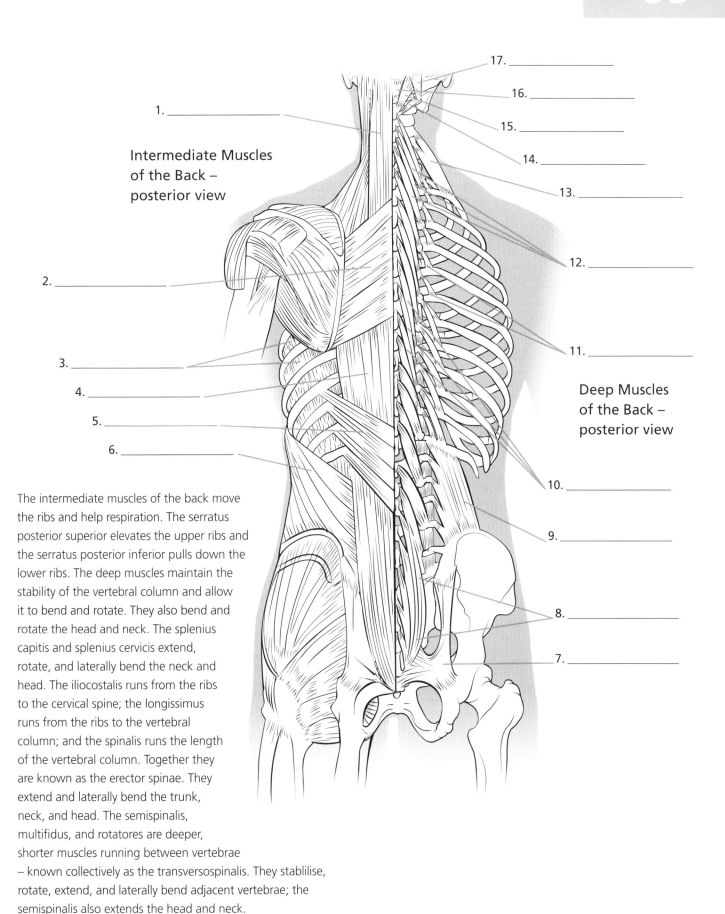

Intermediate Muscles of the Back – posterior view

1. _____

2. _____

3. _____

4. _____

5. _____

6. _____

Deep Muscles of the Back – posterior view

17. _____

16. _____

15. _____

14. _____

13. _____

12. _____

11. _____

10. _____

9. _____

8. _____

7. _____

The intermediate muscles of the back move the ribs and help respiration. The serratus posterior superior elevates the upper ribs and the serratus posterior inferior pulls down the lower ribs. The deep muscles maintain the stability of the vertebral column and allow it to bend and rotate. They also bend and rotate the head and neck. The splenius capitis and splenius cervicis extend, rotate, and laterally bend the neck and head. The iliocostalis runs from the ribs to the cervical spine; the longissimus runs from the ribs to the vertebral column; and the spinalis runs the length of the vertebral column. Together they are known as the erector spinae. They extend and laterally bend the trunk, neck, and head. The semispinalis, multifidus, and rotatores are deeper, shorter muscles running between vertebrae – known collectively as the transversospinalis. They stablilise, rotate, extend, and laterally bend adjacent vertebrae; the semispinalis also extends the head and neck.

Answers

1. Semispinalis capitis, 2. Rhomboid major, 3. External intercostal, 4. Erector spinae, 5. Serratus posterior inferior, 6. Internal oblique, 7. Sacrotuberous ligament, 8. Multifidus, 9. Quadratus lumborum, 10. Semispinalis thoracis, 11. Levatores costarum, 12. Semispinalis cervicis, 13. Scalenus posterior, 14. Oblique capitis inferior, 15. Rectus capitis posterior major, 16. Rectus capitis posterior minor, 17. Oblique capitis superior

Muscles of the Thorax and Abdomen

Superficial and Deep Muscles of the Thorax and Abdomen – anterior view

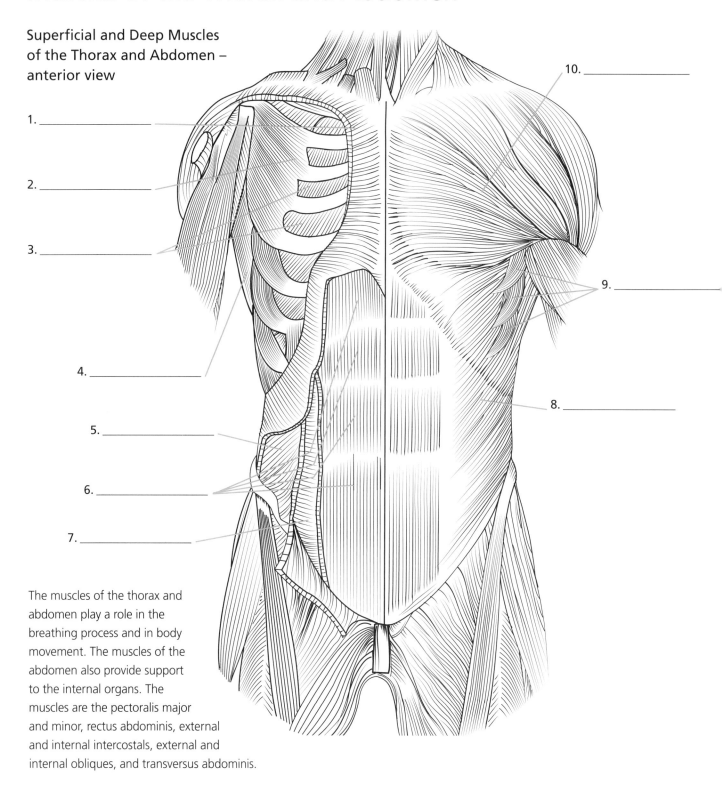

1. _____

2. _____

3. _____

4. _____

5. _____

6. _____

7. _____

10. _____

9. _____

8. _____

The muscles of the thorax and abdomen play a role in the breathing process and in body movement. The muscles of the abdomen also provide support to the internal organs. The muscles are the pectoralis major and minor, rectus abdominis, external and internal intercostals, external and internal obliques, and transversus abdominis.

Answers

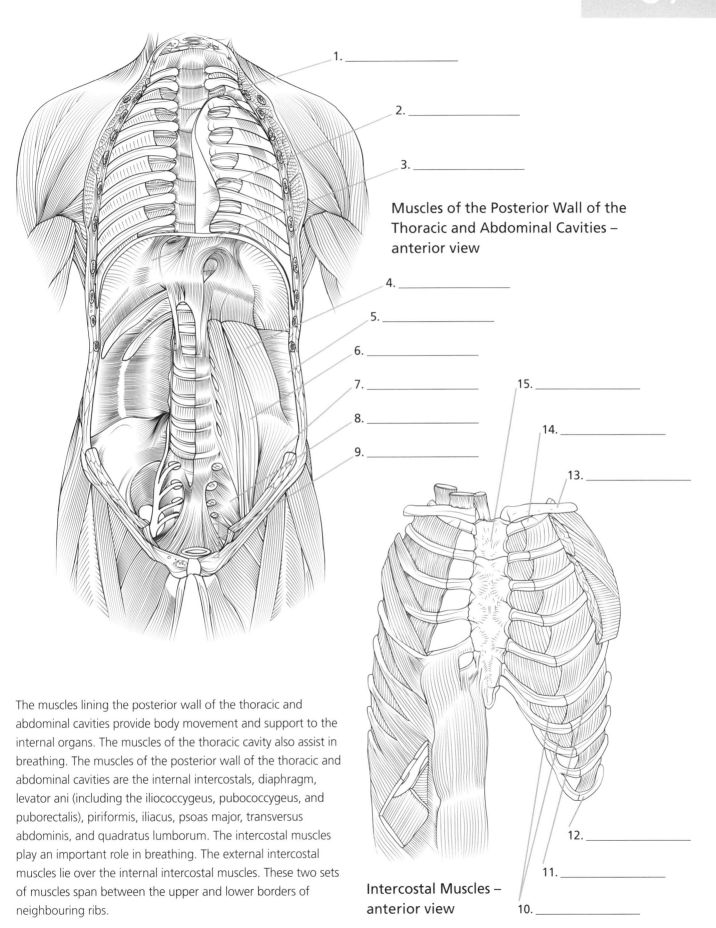

1. _____

2. _____

3. _____

Muscles of the Posterior Wall of the Thoracic and Abdominal Cavities – anterior view

4. _____

5. _____

6. _____

7. _____

8. _____

9. _____

15. _____

14. _____

13. _____

12. _____

11. _____

10. _____

Intercostal Muscles – anterior view

The muscles lining the posterior wall of the thoracic and abdominal cavities provide body movement and support to the internal organs. The muscles of the thoracic cavity also assist in breathing. The muscles of the posterior wall of the thoracic and abdominal cavities are the internal intercostals, diaphragm, levator ani (including the iliococcygeus, pubococcygeus, and puborectalis), piriformis, iliacus, psoas major, transversus abdominis, and quadratus lumborum. The intercostal muscles play an important role in breathing. The external intercostal muscles lie over the internal intercostal muscles. These two sets of muscles span between the upper and lower borders of neighbouring ribs.

Answers

Muscles of the Thorax and Abdomen

The diaphragm is a sheet of muscle that separates the chest cavity from the abdominal cavity, and is pierced by several structures that pass between the two cavities. The three largest of these structures are the oesophagus, the aorta, and the inferior vena cava. The heart and lungs lie on the upper convex surface of the diaphragm, with the pericardial sac firmly attached to the upper surface of the central tendon of the diaphragm, which is the central part of the diaphragm.

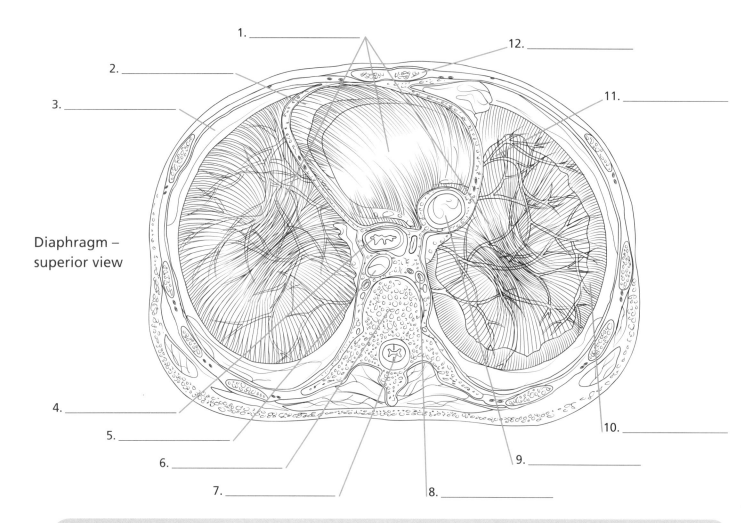

1. _____

2. _____

3. _____

12. _____

11. _____

Diaphragm – superior view

4. _____

5. _____

6. _____

7. _____

8. _____

9. _____

10. _____

Hiatus hernia

A hiatus hernia is the abnormal protrusion of an internal organ through the oesophageal hiatus (opening) in the diaphragm. The most common form is due to sliding of the gastro-oesophageal junction up through the diaphragm into the chest cavity (sliding hiatus hernia). This leads to reflux of stomach contents into the lower oesophagus, causing a burning pain behind the sternum (heartburn). The condition is made worse by abdominal obesity and eating spicy food. Symptoms are relieved by avoiding spicy foods, losing weight, eating smaller meals, sleeping propped up on pillows, and taking antacids. Surgery may be necessary if these measures prove ineffective.

Answers

1. Central tendon of diaphragm, 2. Pericardium (cut), 3. Costal parietal pleura, 4. Oesophagus 5. Aorta, 6. Body of a vertebra, 7. Spinal cord, 8. Azygos vein, 9. Inferior vena cava, 10. Diaphragmatic parietal pleura, 11. Right phrenic nerve, 12. Sternum

The inferior surface of the diaphragm forms the roof of the abdominal cavity and lies over the stomach, on the left, and the liver, on the right. The diaphragm arises at the vertebral column, rib pairs 7–12 along the side of the chest, and the xiphoid process of the sternum, and inserts at the central tendon of the diaphragm.

Diaphragm –
inferior view

10. _____

9. _____

1. _____

2. _____

3. _____

4. _____

5. _____

6. _____

7. _____

8. _____

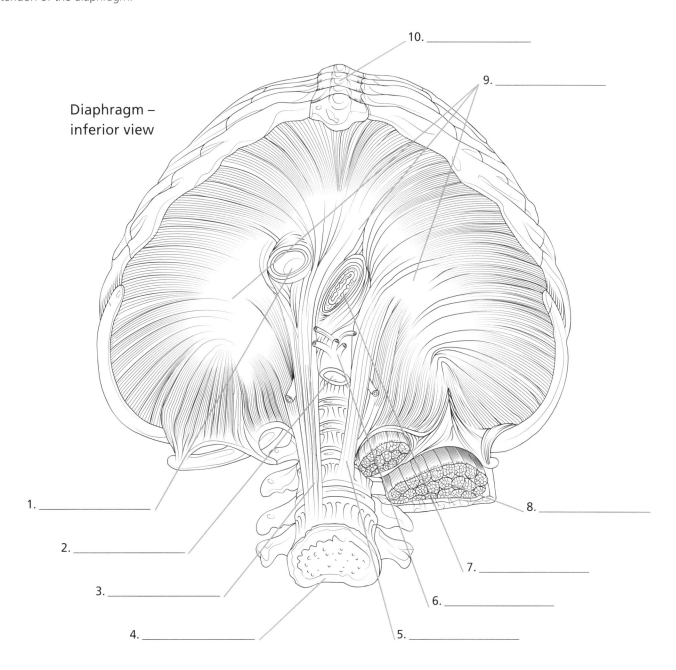

Pelvic Floor Muscles and Muscles of the Perineum

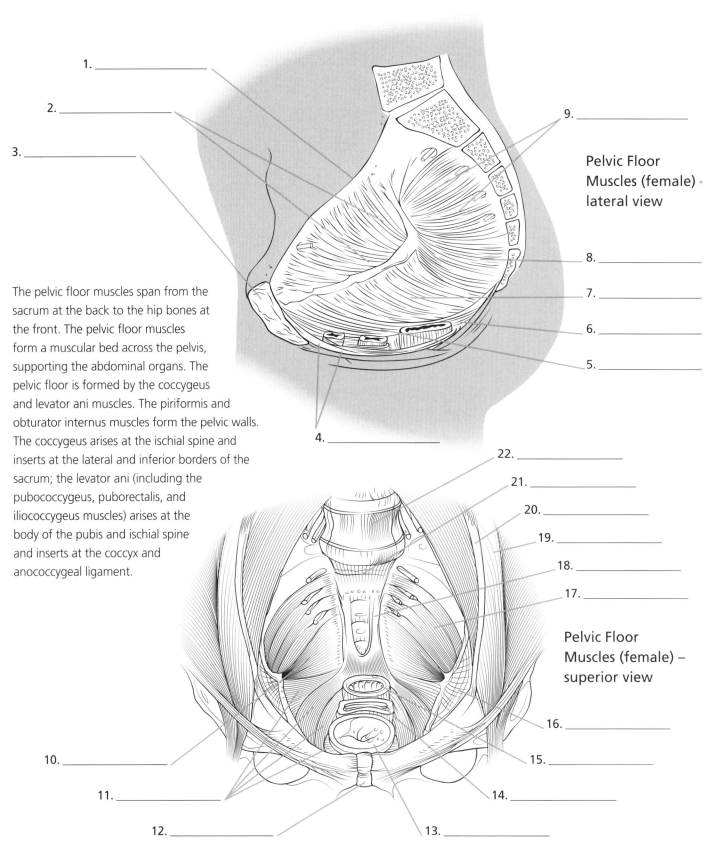

1. _____

2. _____

3. _____

9. _____

Pelvic Floor Muscles (female) – lateral view

8. _____

7. _____

6. _____

5. _____

The pelvic floor muscles span from the sacrum at the back to the hip bones at the front. The pelvic floor muscles form a muscular bed across the pelvis, supporting the abdominal organs. The pelvic floor is formed by the coccygeus and levator ani muscles. The piriformis and obturator internus muscles form the pelvic walls. The coccygeus arises at the ischial spine and inserts at the lateral and inferior borders of the sacrum; the levator ani (including the pubococcygeus, puborectalis, and iliococcygeus muscles) arises at the body of the pubis and ischial spine and inserts at the coccyx and anococcygeal ligament.

4. _____

22. _____

21. _____

20. _____

19. _____

18. _____

17. _____

Pelvic Floor Muscles (female) – superior view

16. _____

15. _____

10. _____

11. _____

14. _____

12. _____

13. _____

Answers

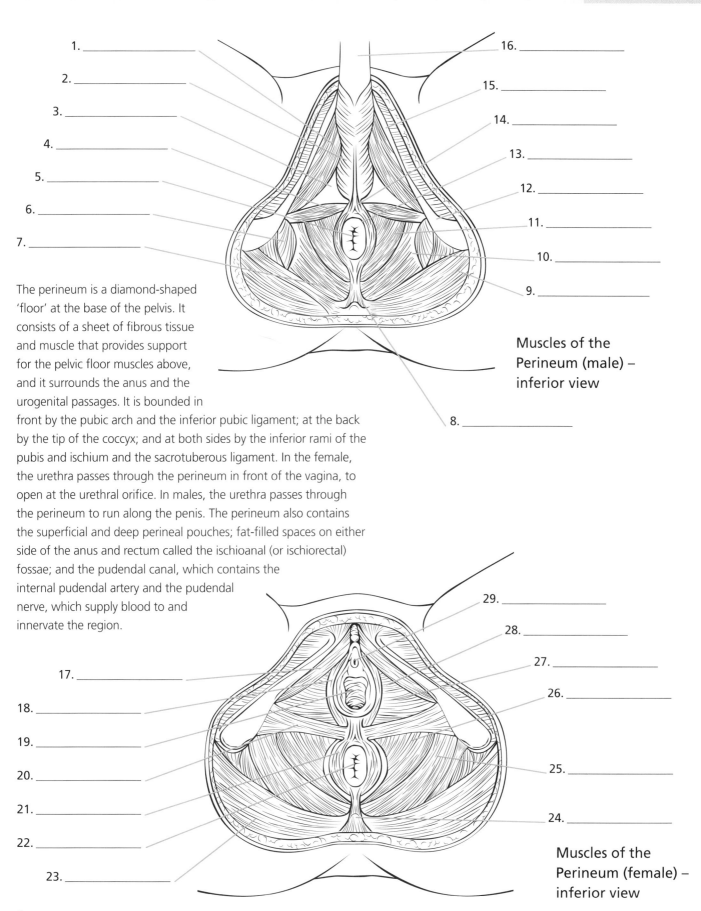

1. _____

2. _____

3. _____

4. _____

5. _____

6. _____

7. _____

16. _____

15. _____

14. _____

13. _____

12. _____

11. _____

10. _____

9. _____

8. _____

The perineum is a diamond-shaped 'floor' at the base of the pelvis. It consists of a sheet of fibrous tissue and muscle that provides support for the pelvic floor muscles above, and it surrounds the anus and the urogenital passages. It is bounded in front by the pubic arch and the inferior pubic ligament; at the back by the tip of the coccyx; and at both sides by the inferior rami of the pubis and ischium and the sacrotuberous ligament. In the female, the urethra passes through the perineum in front of the vagina, to open at the urethral orifice. In males, the urethra passes through the perineum to run along the penis. The perineum also contains the superficial and deep perineal pouches; fat-filled spaces on either side of the anus and rectum called the ischioanal (or ischiorectal) fossae; and the pudendal canal, which contains the internal pudendal artery and the pudendal nerve, which supply blood to and innervate the region.

Muscles of the Perineum (male) – inferior view

17. _____

18. _____

19. _____

20. _____

21. _____

22. _____

23. _____

29. _____

28. _____

27. _____

26. _____

25. _____

24. _____

Muscles of the Perineum (female) – inferior view

Answers

Muscles of the Shoulder

Superficial and Deep
Muscles of the Shoulder –
posterior view

1. _____

2. _____

8. _____

7. _____

6. _____

5. _____

4. _____

3. _____

The pectoral girdle has two groups of muscles: one group attaches the humerus to the shoulder girdle, and the other attaches the shoulder girdle to the trunk. The trapezius, deltoid, and latissimus dorsi are superficial muscles; the infraspinatus, rhomboid major and minor, and supraspinatus are deep muscles. The trapezius arises at the occipital bone and spinous processes from the lowest cervical vertebra to the lowest thoracic vertebra (C7–T12) and inserts at the clavicle and acromion and spine of the scapula; the deltoid arises at the clavicle and acromion and spine of the scapula and inserts at the deltoid tuberosity of the humerus; the latissimus dorsi arises at the spinous processes of the lower vertebrae, thoracolumbar fascia, and rib pairs 8–12 and inserts at the intertubercular groove of the humerus; and the infraspinatus and supraspinatus arise at the scapula and insert at the greater tubercle of the humerus. The rhomboid major arises at the spinous processes of thoracic vertebrae T2–T5; the rhomboid minor arises at the spinous processes of the last cervical vertebra and first thoracic vertebra (C7–T1); and both insert at the medial border of the scapula.

Answers

Superficial and Deep
Muscles of the Shoulder –
anterior view

1. _____

4. _____

3. _____

2. _____

Superficial Muscles
of the Shoulder –
lateral view

5. _____

6. _____

7. _____

As a general rule, the muscles that pass in front of the shoulder joint act to flex or rotate the humerus. The pectoralis minor arises at rib pairs 2–5 and inserts at the coracoid process of the scapula; the pectoralis major arises at the clavicle, sternum, and cartilages of rib pairs 2–6 and inserts at the greater tubercle of the humerus; the deltoid arises at the clavicle and acromion and spine of the scapula and inserts at the deltoid tuberosity of the humerus; the trapezius arises at the occipital bone and spinous processes from the lowest cervical vertebra to the lowest thoracic vertebrae (C7–T12) and inserts at the clavicle and acromion and spine of the scapula; and the serratus anterior arises at rib pairs 1–8 and inserts at the medial border of the scapula.

Answers

Muscles of the Upper Limb

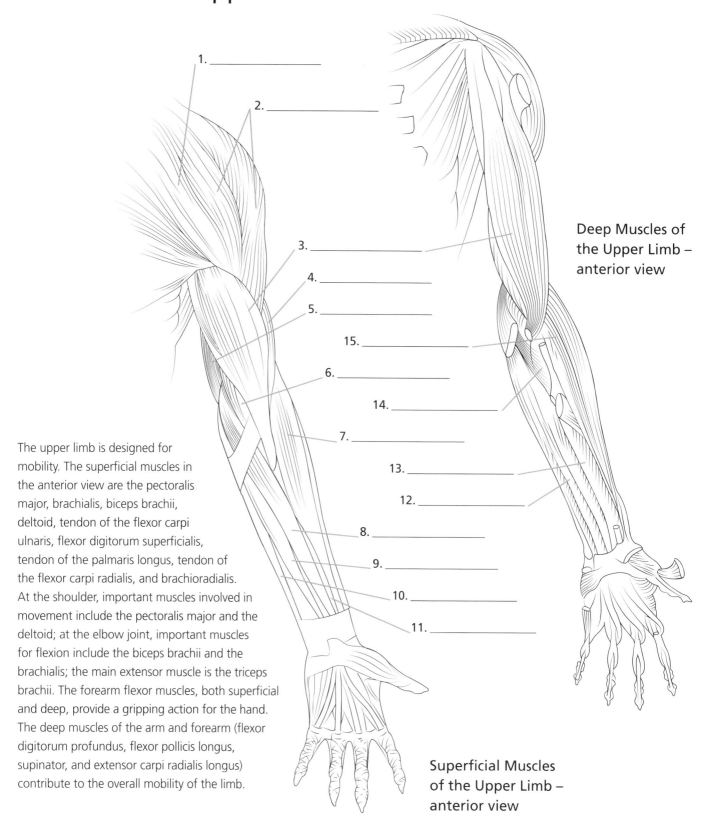

1. _____

2. _____

3. _____

4. _____

5. _____

15. _____

6. _____

14. _____

7. _____

13. _____

12. _____

8. _____

9. _____

10. _____

11. _____

Deep Muscles of
the Upper Limb –
anterior view

The upper limb is designed for mobility. The superficial muscles in the anterior view are the pectoralis major, brachialis, biceps brachii, deltoid, tendon of the flexor carpi ulnaris, flexor digitorum superficialis, tendon of the palmaris longus, tendon of the flexor carpi radialis, and brachioradialis. At the shoulder, important muscles involved in movement include the pectoralis major and the deltoid; at the elbow joint, important muscles for flexion include the biceps brachii and the brachialis; the main extensor muscle is the triceps brachii. The forearm flexor muscles, both superficial and deep, provide a gripping action for the hand. The deep muscles of the arm and forearm (flexor digitorum profundus, flexor pollicis longus, supinator, and extensor carpi radialis longus) contribute to the overall mobility of the limb.

Superficial Muscles
of the Upper Limb –
anterior view

Answers
1. Pectoralis major, 2. Deltoid, 3. Biceps brachii, 4. Brachialis, 5. Triceps brachii, 6. Pronator teres, 7. Brachioradialis, 8. Tendon of flexor carpi radialis, 9. Tendon of palmaris longus, 10. Tendon of flexor carpi ulnaris, 11. Flexor digitorum superficialis, 12. Flexor digitorum profundus, 13. Flexor pollicis longus, 14. Supinator, 15. Extensor carpi radialis longus

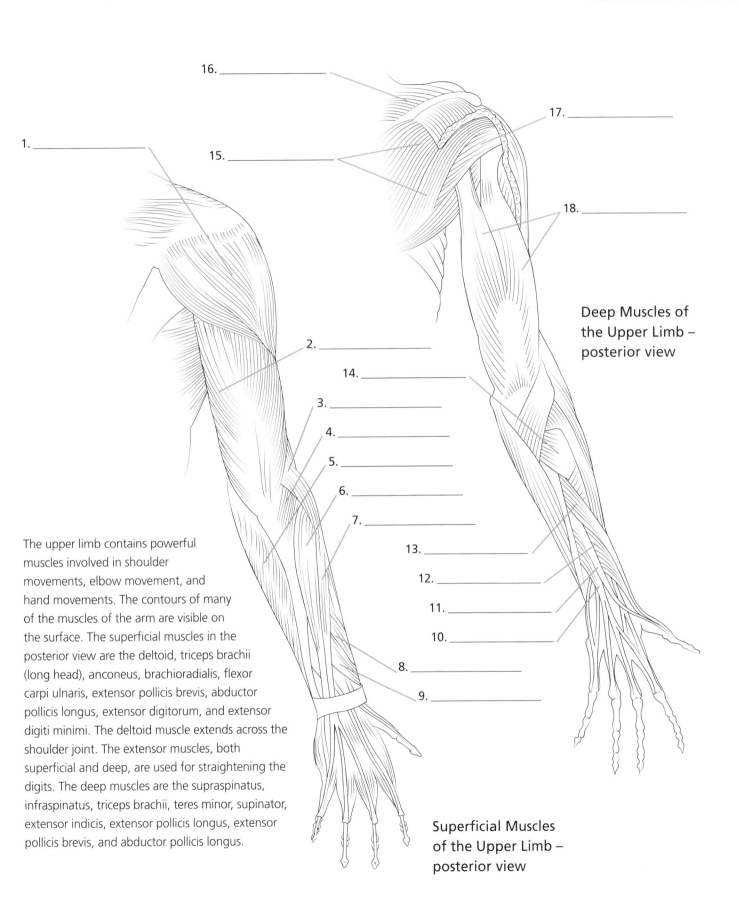

16. _____

17. _____

1. _____

15. _____

18. _____

Deep Muscles of the Upper Limb – posterior view

2. _____

14. _____

3. _____

4. _____

5. _____

6. _____

7. _____

13. _____

12. _____

11. _____

10. _____

8. _____

9. _____

The upper limb contains powerful muscles involved in shoulder movements, elbow movement, and hand movements. The contours of many of the muscles of the arm are visible on the surface. The superficial muscles in the posterior view are the deltoid, triceps brachii (long head), anconeus, brachioradialis, flexor carpi ulnaris, extensor pollicis brevis, abductor pollicis longus, extensor digitorum, and extensor digiti minimi. The deltoid muscle extends across the shoulder joint. The extensor muscles, both superficial and deep, are used for straightening the digits. The deep muscles are the supraspinatus, infraspinatus, triceps brachii, teres minor, supinator, extensor indicis, extensor pollicis longus, extensor pollicis brevis, and abductor pollicis longus.

Superficial Muscles of the Upper Limb – posterior view

Answers

Muscles of the Upper Limb

The lateral view of the superficial muscles of the upper limb shows the deltoid, lateral head of the triceps brachii, brachialis, biceps brachii, brachioradialis, extensor carpi radialis longus, extensor digitorum, flexor carpi ulnaris, and extensor carpi ulnaris. The lateral view of the elbow shows the muscles of the arm and the extensor muscles of the forearm. The triceps brachii causes elbow extension, while the biceps brachii is responsible for elbow flexion and participates in supination of the forearm. The brachialis and brachioradialis also contribute to elbow flexion.

Superficial Muscles of the Upper Limb – lateral view

9. _____

8. _____

7. _____

1. _____

2. _____

3. _____

4. _____

5. _____

6. _____

12. _____

11. _____

10. _____

19. _____

13. _____

14. _____

15. _____

16. _____

17. _____

18. _____

Muscles of the Elbow – lateral view

Answers

1. Biceps brachii, 2. Brachioradialis, 3. Extensor carpi radialis longus, 4. Extensor digitorum, 5. Extensor carpi ulnaris, 6. Flexor carpi ulnaris, 7. Brachialis, 8. lateral head of triceps brachii, 9. Deltoid, 10. Brachialis, 11. Biceps brachii, 12. Deltoid, 13. Tendon of triceps brachii, 14. Olecranon, 15. Extensor carpi ulnaris, 16. Extensor carpi ulnaris, 17. Extensor digitorum, 18. Extensor carpi radialis longus, 19. Brachioradialis

Muscles of the Elbow – anterior view

1. _____

2. _____

3. _____

4. _____

5. _____

6. _____

7. _____

8. _____

9. _____

10. _____

11. _____

12. _____

13. _____

14. _____

15. _____

16. _____

17. _____

18. _____

19. _____

Muscles of the Elbow – posterior view

The anterior view of the muscles of the elbow shows the triceps brachii, biceps brachii, brachioradialis, pronator teres, flexor carpi radialis, biceps brachii tendon, brachialis, palmaris longus, flexor digitorum superficialis, flexor carpi ulnaris, brachialis tendon, and common flexor tendon. The posterior view shows the brachialis, triceps brachii, brachioradialis, extensor carpi radialis brevis, common extensor tendon, flexor digitorum superficialis, and flexor carpi ulnaris. The elbow joint separates the humerus of the upper arm from the forearm bones – the radius and ulna. This relatively stable synovial hinge joint allows the forearm to flex and extend at the elbow. Important muscles for flexion include the biceps brachii and brachialis, while the main extensor muscle is the triceps brachii. The anterior forearm muscles, extending from the elbow to the hand, allow rotation of the forearm, from supination to pronation, flexion of the hand at the wrist, and flexion of the digits. Located at the back of the forearm are the muscles dedicated to extension of the hand at the wrist and flexion of the digits.

Answers

1. Biceps brachii, 2. Brachialis tendon, 3. Pronator teres, 4. Flexor carpi radialis, 5. Biceps brachii tendon, 6. Palmaris longus, 7. Flexor digitorum superficialis, 8. Common extensor tendon, 9. Flexor carpi ulnaris, 10. Extensor carpi radialis brevis, 11. Lateral epicondyle of humerus, 12. Common flexor tendons, 13. Brachioradialis, 14. Brachialis, 15. Triceps brachii, 16. Radius, 17. Ulna, 18. Medial epicondyle, 19. Humerus

Muscles of the Upper Limb

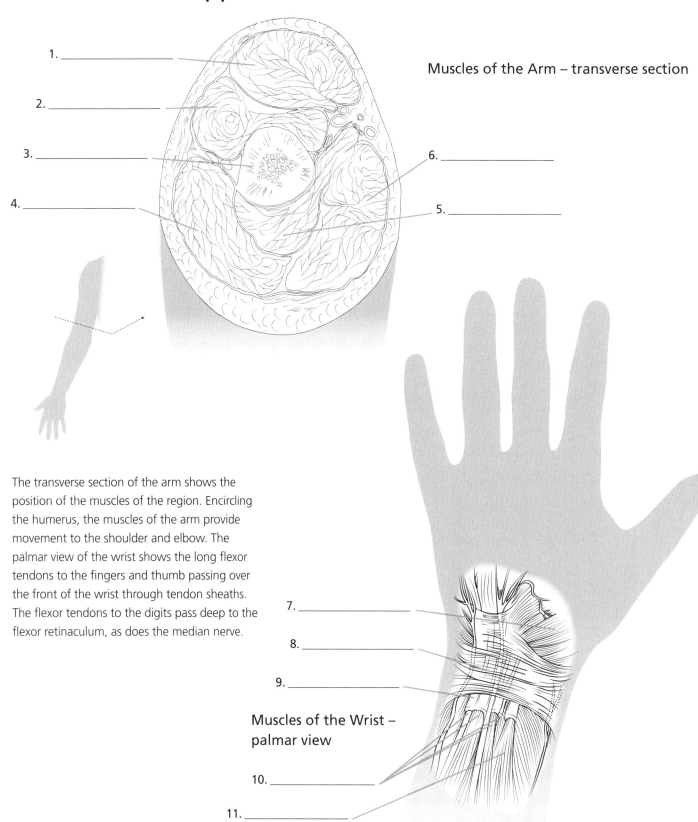

Muscles of the Arm – transverse section

1. _____

2. _____

3. _____

4. _____

6. _____

5. _____

The transverse section of the arm shows the position of the muscles of the region. Encircling the humerus, the muscles of the arm provide movement to the shoulder and elbow. The palmar view of the wrist shows the long flexor tendons to the fingers and thumb passing over the front of the wrist through tendon sheaths. The flexor tendons to the digits pass deep to the flexor retinaculum, as does the median nerve.

7. _____

8. _____

9. _____

Muscles of the Wrist – palmar view

10. _____

11. _____

Answers

1. Biceps brachii, 2. Brachialis, 3. Humerus, 4. Triceps brachii (lateral head) 5. Triceps brachii (medial head), 6. Triceps brachii (long head), 7. Thenar muscles, 8. Flexor retinaculum, 9. Tendinous sheath of flexor digitorum superficialis, 10. Flexor digitorum superficialis tendons, 11. Flexor carpi radialis

Muscles of the Wrist and Hand – dorsal view

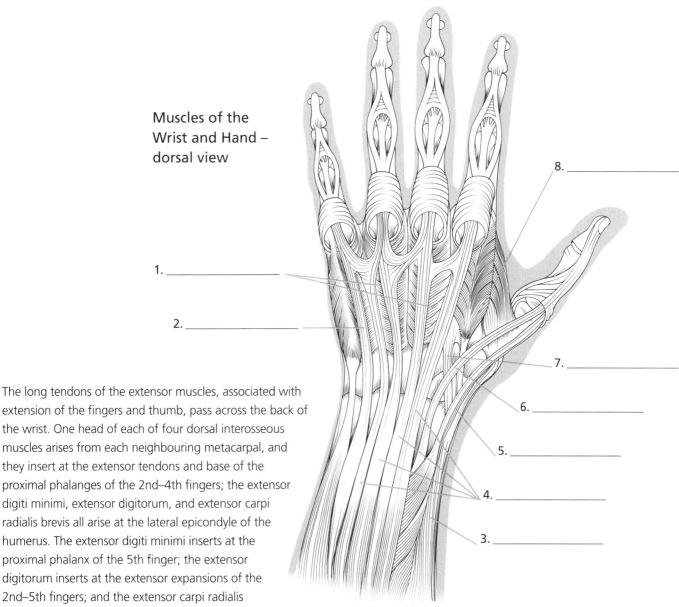

8. _____

1. _____

2. _____

7. _____

6. _____

5. _____

4. _____

3. _____

The long tendons of the extensor muscles, associated with extension of the fingers and thumb, pass across the back of the wrist. One head of each of four dorsal interosseous muscles arises from each neighbouring metacarpal, and they insert at the extensor tendons and base of the proximal phalanges of the 2nd–4th fingers; the extensor digiti minimi, extensor digitorum, and extensor carpi radialis brevis all arise at the lateral epicondyle of the humerus. The extensor digiti minimi inserts at the proximal phalanx of the 5th finger; the extensor digitorum inserts at the extensor expansions of the 2nd–5th fingers; and the extensor carpi radialis brevis at the base of the 2nd metacarpal bone. The abductor pollicis longus arises at the posterior of the proximal end of the radius and ulna and inserts at the base of the 1st metacarpal bone; the extensor pollicis brevis arises at the posterior of the radius and inserts at the base of the proximal phalanx of the thumb; the extensor pollicis longus arises at the posterior of the ulna and the interosseous membrane and inserts at the base of the distal phalanx of the thumb; and the extensor carpi radialis longus arises at the lateral supracondylar ridge of the humerus and inserts at the base of the 2nd metacarpal bone.

Answers

1. Dorsal interosseous muscles, 2. Extensor digiti minimi, 3. Abductor pollicis longus, 4. Extensor digitorum, 5. Extensor pollicis brevis, 6. Extensor pollicis longus, 7. Extensor carpi radialis brevis, 8. Extensor carpi radialis longus

Muscles of the Lower Limb

1. _____

2. _____

3. _____

4. _____

5. _____

6. _____

7. _____

8. _____

9. _____

10. _____

15. _____

16. _____

17. _____

14. _____

18. _____

13. _____

12. _____

11. _____

27. _____

26. _____

25. _____

24. _____

23. _____

22. _____

21. _____

20. _____

19. _____

Superficial Muscles of the Lower Limb – anterior view

Deep Muscles of the Lower Limb – anterior view

The superficial muscles of the lower limb are powerful and participate in locomotion. The quadriceps femoris muscle forms the major muscle mass of the front and outer side of the thigh. Its four parts are the rectus femoris, vastus lateralis, vastus medialis, and vastus intermedius. The anterior compartment of the leg contains the muscles that move the foot upwards (dorsiflex the ankle). The lateral compartment contains the fibularis longus and fibularis brevis muscles, which are responsible for turning the sole of the foot outwards (eversion). The deep muscles of the thigh include the adductor muscles (adductor magnus, adductor longus, and adductor brevis). The muscles act to rotate, flex, and adduct the thigh. The extensor muscles (extensor hallucis longus and extensor digitorum longus) are the deep muscles of the leg, acting to extend the foot at the ankle (dorsiflex the ankle) and the toes.

Answers

1. Tensor fasciae latae, 2. Iliopsoas, 3. Sartorius, 4. Adductor longus, 5. Rectus femoris, 6. Vastus lateralis, 7. Iliotibial tract, 8. Fibularis longus, 9. Tibialis anterior, 10. Extensor digitorum longus, 11. Soleus, 12. Gastrocnemius, 13. Vastus medialis, 14. Gracilis, 15. Pectineus, 16. Adductor longus (cut), 17. Vastus intermedius, 18. Iliotibial tract, 19. Tibialis anterior (cut), 20. Extensor hallucis longus, 21. Tibialis anterior (cut), 22. Rectus femoris (cut), 23. Adductor magnus, 24. Adductor longus (cut), 25. Adductor brevis, 26. Adductor longus (cut), 27. Sartorius (cut)

1. _____

2. _____

10. _____

11. _____

12. _____

13. _____

22. _____

9. _____

8. _____

7. _____

6. _____

21. _____

20. _____

19. _____

14. _____

3. _____

5. _____

4. _____

15. _____

16. _____

18. _____

17. _____

Superficial Muscles of the Lower Limb – posterior view

Deep Muscles of the Lower Limb – posterior view

Powerful superficial muscles surround and stabilise the hip region; the gluteal region is dominated by the gluteus maximus, the largest muscle in the body. The hamstring muscles in the posterior compartment of the thigh include the semimembranosus, semitendinosus, and the long head of the biceps femoris, which together extend the hip joint and flex the knee joint. The superficial group of the posterior compartment of the calf region contains the powerful gastrocnemius and soleus muscles, both critical for pushing off from the ground. The medial compartment of the thigh contains the adductor muscles, which pull the leg towards the midline. In the posterior compartment of the calf, the deep group of muscles pass behind the ankle joint and attach to the bones of the foot. The largest of these, the flexor hallucis longus, is critical to pushing off with the big toe during walking.

Answers

1. Gluteus medius, 2. Gluteus maximus, 3. Gastrocnemius (medial head), 4. Soleus, 5. Gastrocnemius (lateral head), 6. Gracilis, 7. Semimembranosus, 8. Biceps femoris, 9. Adductor magnus (hamstring), 10. Superior gemellus, 11. Piriformis, 12. Inferior gemellus, 13. Quadratus femoris, 14. Plantaris, 15. Tibialis posterior, 16. Flexor digitorum longus, 17. Flexor hallucis longus, 18. Fibularis longus, 19. Popliteus, 20. Biceps femoris (short head), 21. Adductor magnus (adductor part), 22. Gluteus minimus.

Muscles of the Lower Limb

Posterior

Medial

Anterior

1. _____
2. _____
3. _____
4. _____

**Muscles of the Thigh –
transverse section**

11. _____
10. _____
9. _____
8. _____
7. _____
6. _____
5. _____

12. _____
13. _____

**Superficial Muscles
of the Lower Limb –
lateral view**

14. _____
15. _____

24. _____
23. _____
22. _____
21. _____
20. _____
19. _____
18. _____
17. _____
16. _____

The thigh is divided into three compartments: anterior, medial, and posterior. The anterior compartment is the location of the muscles that flex the hip and/or extend the knee. The muscles of the medial compartment adduct the knee. The muscles of the posterior compartment extend the hip and/or flex the knee. The transverse section shows the superficial and deep muscles found in the thigh region. The thigh contains the quadriceps femoris, hamstring, and adductor muscles. The lateral view of the muscles of the lower limb shows the sartorius, quadriceps femoris (vastus lateralis), tibialis anterior, extensor digitorum longus, gluteus maximus, iliotibial tract, lateral head of the gastrocnemius, fibularis longus, soleus, superior extensor retinaculum, inferior extensor retinaculum, Achilles tendon (tendo calcaneus), and superior fibularis retinaculum.

Answers

1. Semitendinosus, 2. Biceps femoris, 3. Vastus lateralis, 4. Vastus intermedius, 5. Rectus femoris, 6. Vastus medialis, 7. Adductor longus, 8. Sartorius, 9. Gracilis, 10. Adductor magnus, 11. Semimembranosus, 12. Sartorius, 13. Quadriceps (vastus lateralis), 14. Tibialis anterior, 15. Extensor digitorum longus, 16. Achilles tendon, 17. Inferior extensor retinaculum, 18. Superior extensor retinaculum, 19. Soleus, 20. Fibularis longus, 21. Lateral head of gastrocnemius, 22. Iliotibial tract, 23. Tensor fasciae latae, 24. Gluteus maximus

1. _____
2. _____
3. _____
4. _____
5. _____
6. _____
7. _____
8. _____
9. _____
10. _____
11. _____

15. _____
14. _____
13. _____
12. _____

Muscles of the Foot – lateral view

16. _____
17. _____
18. _____
19. _____
20. _____
21. _____
22. _____

Muscles of the Foot – posteromedial view

23. _____

The main muscles producing dorsiflexion of the foot (bringing the upper surface of the foot closer to the front of the leg) arise at the front of the leg, while the main muscles producing plantarflexion (raising the heel from the ground, as in pointing the toes) arise at the back of the leg. Between the toes are the deepest muscles, the interosseous muscles, which act to abduct (dorsal interossei) or adduct (plantar interossei) the toes. Many of the muscles of the leg converge at the ankle, thin into tendons, and then extend across the front, back, and sides of the ankle. Tendon sheaths protect the tendons as they pass across the ankle joint. Lying at the back of the ankle is the Achilles (calcaneal) tendon.

28. _____
27. _____
26. _____
25. _____
24. _____

Answers

1. Extensor hallucis longus, 2. Extensor digitorum longus, 3. Superior extensor retinaculum, 4. Achilles (calcaneal) tendon, 5. Tendon sheaths, 6. Superior fibular retinaculum, 7. Inferior fibular retinaculum, 8. Fibularis longus tendon, 9. Extensor digitorum brevis, 10. Fibularis brevis tendon, 11. Fibularis tertius, 12. Extensor hallucis longus tendon, 13. Extensor digitorum brevis tendons, 14. Extensor digitorum longus tendons, 15. Inferior extensor retinaculum, 16. Flexor hallucis longus tendon, 17. Tibialis posterior, 18. Flexor digitorum longus, 19. Tibia, 20. Flexor hallucis longus, 21. Tibialis posterior longus tendon, 22. Flexor retinaculum, 23. First metatarsal, 24. Calcaneal tuberosity, 25. Achilles (calcaneal) tendon, 26. Flexor hallucis longus tendon, 27. Fibularis longus tendon, 28. Fibularis brevis tendon

Muscles of the Lower Limb

The muscles of the foot move the foot during walking, standing, running, and jumping. They also help to maintain the arches of the foot. The muscles are arranged in four layers. In the first (superficial) layer, the abductor hallucis flexes and abducts the big toe and supports the medial longitudinal arch. The flexor digitorum brevis attaches to and flexes the lateral four toes and supports the medial and lateral longitudinal arches. The abductor digiti minimi flexes and abducts the fifth toe and supports the lateral longitudinal arch. In the second, deeper layer are the flexor tendons that flex the toes: the flexor hallucis longus (the big toe) and the flexor digitorum longus (the other four lateral toes). The quadratus plantae (or flexor accessorius) also helps to flex the lateral four toes. The lumbricals help to extend the toes during walking and running.

6. _____

5. _____

4. _____

**First Layer
Muscles of the Foot –
inferior view**

1. _____

2. _____

13. _____

7. _____

8. _____

9. _____

10. _____

12. _____

3. _____

11. _____

**Second Layer
Muscles of the Foot –
inferior view**

Answers

1. Flexor digitorum brevis, 2. Abductor hallucis, 3. Fibrous flexor sheaths, 4. Abductor digiti minimi, 5. Plantar aponeurosis (cut), 6. Calcaneus, 7. Calcaneus, 8. Flexor digitorum longus tendon, 9. Flexor hallucis longus tendon, 10. Flexor hallucis brevis, 11. Lumbricals, 12. Flexor digiti minimi brevis, 13. Quadratus plantae

In the third layer is the flexor hallucis brevis, a short muscle that flexes the big toe and supports the medial longitudinal arch. There is adductor hallucis, the oblique head of which adducts the big toe and supports the transverse arch and the transverse head of which adducts the big toe. The flexor digiti minimi brevis flexes the little toe. In the fourth (deepest) layer of muscles, between the metatarsal bones of the foot, are the interossei. There are four dorsal interossei, which abduct the toes, and three plantar interossei, which adduct the toes.

5. _____

**Third Layer
Muscles of the Foot –
inferior view**

1. _____

2. _____

3. _____

12. _____

4. _____

6. _____

7. _____

8. _____

9. _____

11. _____

10. _____

**Fourth Layer
Muscles of the Foot – inferior view**

Answers

Nervous System

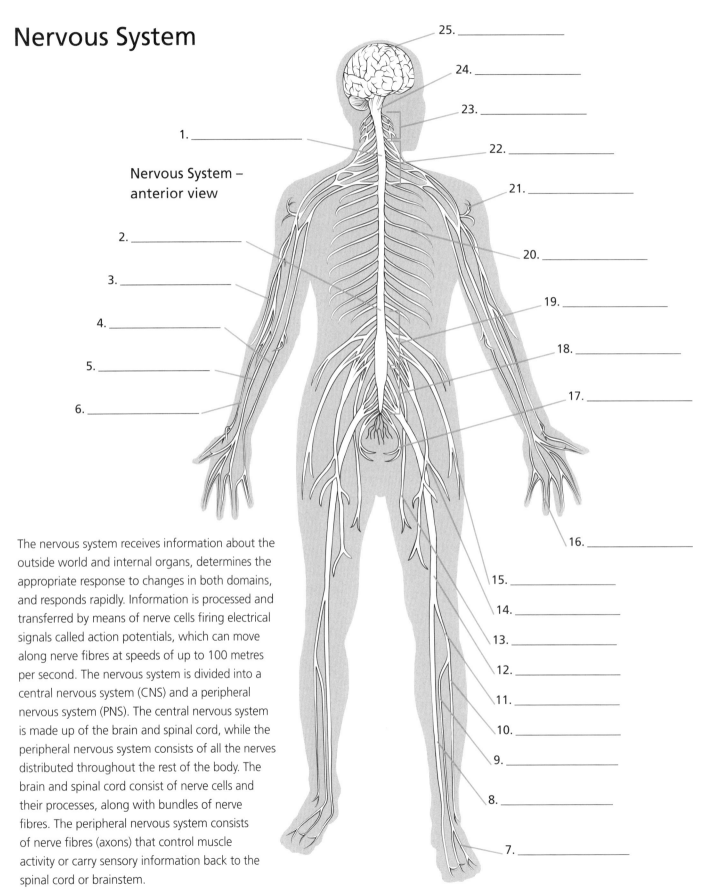

**Nervous System –
anterior view**

1. _____

2. _____

3. _____

4. _____

5. _____

6. _____

7. _____

8. _____

9. _____

10. _____

11. _____

12. _____

13. _____

14. _____

15. _____

16. _____

17. _____

18. _____

19. _____

20. _____

21. _____

22. _____

23. _____

24. _____

25. _____

The nervous system receives information about the outside world and internal organs, determines the appropriate response to changes in both domains, and responds rapidly. Information is processed and transferred by means of nerve cells firing electrical signals called action potentials, which can move along nerve fibres at speeds of up to 100 metres per second. The nervous system is divided into a central nervous system (CNS) and a peripheral nervous system (PNS). The central nervous system is made up of the brain and spinal cord, while the peripheral nervous system consists of all the nerves distributed throughout the rest of the body. The brain and spinal cord consist of nerve cells and their processes, along with bundles of nerve fibres. The peripheral nervous system consists of nerve fibres (axons) that control muscle activity or carry sensory information back to the spinal cord or brainstem.

Answers

1. Cervical enlargement of spinal cord, 2. Lumbosacral enlargement of spinal cord, 3. Musculocutaneous nerve, 4. Ulnar nerve, 5. Median nerve, 6. Radial nerve, 7. Plantar nerve, 8. Posterior tibial nerve, 9. Deep fibular nerve, 10. Superficial fibular nerve, 11. Common fibular nerve, 12. Sciatic nerve, 13. Obturator nerve, 14. Femoral nerve, 15. Lateral femoral cutaneous nerve, 16. Digital nerve, 17. Pudendal nerve, 18. Sacral plexus, 19. Lumbar plexus, 20. Intercostal nerve, 21. Axillary nerve, 22. Brachial plexus, 23. Cervical plexus, 24. Medulla oblongata, 25. Cerebral hemisphere

1. _____

2. _____

Neuron

3. _____

4. _____

10. _____

9. _____

8. _____

7. _____

6. _____

5. _____

Neurons are nerve cells that are specially designed to conduct nerve impulses to and from all parts of the body. A typical nerve cell has a cell body with a nucleus and a number of branching processes (dendrites), which receive incoming information, and an outgoing fibre (axon), which carries information away from the nerve cell body. Nerves connect the brain and the spinal cord (central nervous system) with peripheral regions such as the muscles, skin, and viscera (peripheral nervous system). The role of nerves is to carry signals that provide us with sensations or control our muscles and organs. The spinal cord is a cylindrical structure that occupies the vertebral canal. In the adult, the lower end of the spinal cord (conus medullaris) is usually located at the level of the L1 or L2 vertebra. Below this, the vertebral canal is occupied largely by the elongated rootlets of the lumbar and sacral spinal nerves (cauda equina).

16. _____

15. _____

14. _____

13. _____

12. _____

11. _____

Central Nervous System –
sagittal view

Answers

1. Synaptic knob, 2. Axon terminal, 3. Dendrite, 5. Myelin sheath, 4. Axon, 5. Dendrite, 6. Mitochondria, 7. Nucleolus, 8. Nuclear membrane, 9. Golgi apparatus, 10. Cell body, 11. Region of cauda equina, 12. Conus medullaris, 13. Spinal cord, 14. Cerebellum, 15. Pons, 16. Cerebrum

Brain and Brain Functions

The brain lies within the cranial cavity of the skull and is made up of hundreds of billions of nerve cells (neurons) and supporting cells (glia). The brain has grey matter (neurons and glia) and white matter (myelin). The human brain can be divided into four main parts: the cerebrum, diencephalon, brainstem, and cerebellum. The largest part is the cerebrum. It is formed by the cerebral hemispheres, which are joined together by a massive bundle of white matter (the corpus callosum), and it is covered by the grey matter of the cerebral cortex. The diencephalon lies beneath the cerebral hemispheres and has two main structures: the thalamus and the hypothalamus. The transverse section of the brain shows the grey matter of the cerebral cortex and the white matter that lies beneath the cortex. Forming the outer layer of the hemispheres of the brain, the cerebral cortex is a highly folded sheet of grey matter, with gyri folding outwards and fissures and sulci folding inwards. The meninges are three concentric protective membranes surrounding the brain and spinal cord. The outermost, the dura mater, is a tough fibrous layer. The middle membrane, the arachnoid mater, is a fragile network of collagen and elastin fibres. The innermost, the pia mater, is a delicate layer of collagen and elastic fibres containing many blood vessels.

Brain – lateral view

1. _____

5. _____

2. _____

3. _____

4. _____

6. _____

7. _____

8. _____

Brain – sagittal view

9. _____

8. _____

7. _____

6. _____

5. _____

4. _____

3. _____

2. _____

Brain – transverse section

1. _____

20. _____

Meninges

10. _____

11. _____

12. _____

13. _____

14. _____

15. _____

16. _____

17. _____

18. _____

19. _____

Answers

Brain and Brain Functions

The brain is divided longitudinally into two hemispheres by the sagittal fissure, with each hemisphere then divided into lobes marked by sulci and fissures in the folds of the cerebral cortex. The central sulcus separates the frontal lobe from the parietal lobe behind it. Located at the back of the brain is the occipital lobe. The temporal lobe lies beneath the frontal and parietal lobes. Each lobe is strongly linked, though not limited, to a particular function. The frontal lobe is involved in movement, thinking, behaviour, and personality; the occipital lobe in the perception of vision; the parietal lobe in the perception of touch and comprehension of speech; and the temporal lobe in memory. The limbic system is a collective term for interconnected brain structures involved in behaviours associated with survival, including the expression of emotion, feeding, drinking, defence, and reproduction, as well as the formation of memory. The system's key components are the hippocampus, amygdala, septal area, and hypothalamus. The brain's four ventricles connect with each other, the central canal of the spinal cord, and the subarachnoid space surrounding the brain and spinal cord. The ventricles and subarachnoid space contain cerebrospinal fluid which acts as a shock absorber, cushioning the brain against mechanical forces.

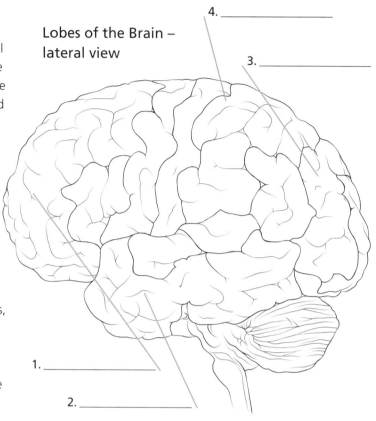

Lobes of the Brain – lateral view

4. _____

3. _____

1. _____

2. _____

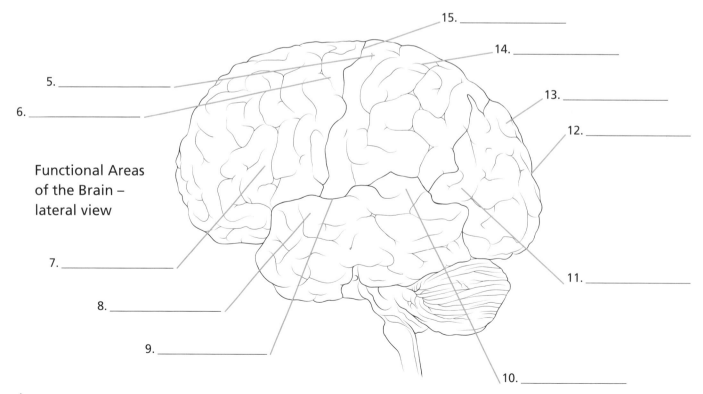

Functional Areas of the Brain – lateral view

5. _____

6. _____

7. _____

8. _____

9. _____

10. _____

15. _____

14. _____

13. _____

12. _____

11. _____

Answers

1. Frontal lobe, 2. Temporal lobe, 3. Occipital lobe, 4. Parietal lobe, 5. Primary somatosensory cortex, 6. Primary motor cortex, 7. Motor speech (Broca's) area, 8. Auditory association area, 9. Primary auditory cortex, 10. Wernicke's sensory speech area, 11. Reading comprehension area, 12. Visual cortex, 13. Visual association area, 14. Somatic sensory association area, 15. Central sulcus

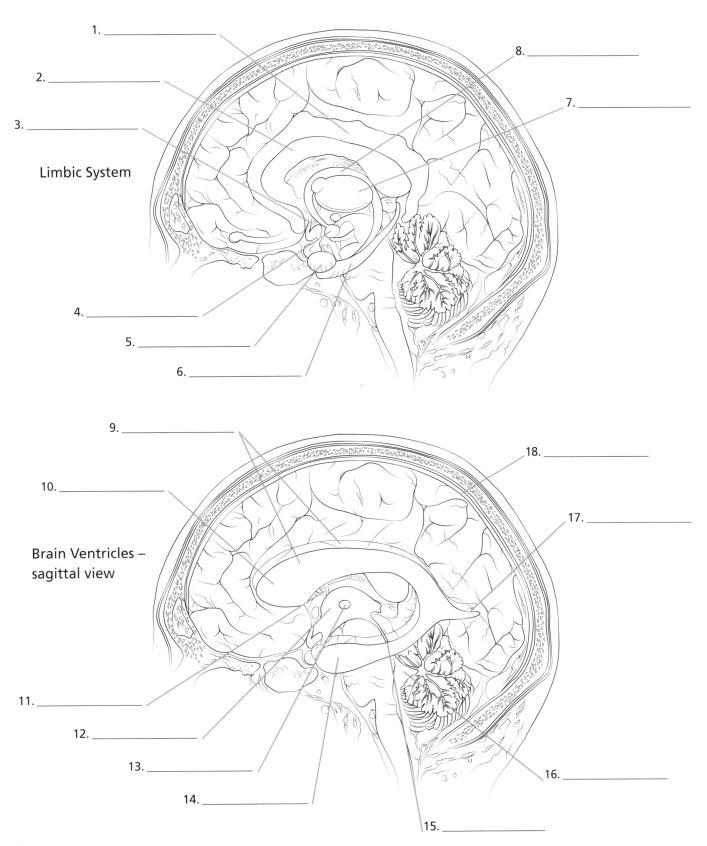

Limbic System

1. _____

2. _____

3. _____

4. _____

5. _____

6. _____

7. _____

8. _____

Brain Ventricles – sagittal view

9. _____

10. _____

11. _____

12. _____

13. _____

14. _____

15. _____

16. _____

17. _____

18. _____

Answers

Cranial Nerves and Brainstem

There are twelve cranial nerves that lead directly from the brain and brainstem to muscles and sensory structures of the head and neck. Some of the cranial nerves also distribute nerves to the organs of the chest and the upper two-thirds of the gastrointestinal tract. Cranial nerve I is the olfactory nerve; cranial nerve II, the optic nerve; cranial nerve III, the oculomotor nerve; cranial nerve IV, the trochlear nerve; cranial nerve V, the trigeminal nerve, which has three sections (the ophthalmic, maxillary, and mandibular divisions); cranial nerve VI is the abducens nerve; cranial nerve VII, the facial nerve; cranial nerve VIII, the vestibulocochlear nerve; cranial nerve IX, the glossopharyngeal nerve; cranial nerve X, the vagus nerve; cranial nerve XI, the spinal accessory nerve; and cranial nerve XII, the hypoglossal nerve.

1. _____
2. _____
3. _____
4. _____
5. _____
6. _____
7. _____
8. _____
9. _____
10. _____
11. _____
12. _____

Cranial Nerves

Answers

1. Olfactory bulb, 2. Optic nerve (II), 3. Oculomotor nerve (III), 4. Trochlear nerve (IV), 5. Trigeminal nerve (V), 6. Abducens nerve (VI), 7. Facial nerve (VII), 8. Vestibulocochlear nerve (VIII), 9. Glossopharyngeal nerve (IX), 10. Vagus nerve (X), 11. Spinal accessory nerve (XI), 12. Hypoglossal nerve (XII)

The brainstem, which is continuous with the spinal cord below it, consists of the midbrain, pons, and medulla. Passing through the brainstem are ascending pathways, carrying sensory information from the spinal cord to the brain, and descending pathways, carrying motor signals down to the spinal cord. The oculomotor (cranial nerve III) and trochlear (IV) nerves arise in the midbrain. The pons lies below the midbrain. Lying below the pons is the medulla oblongata. The hypoglossal (XII), spinal accessory (XI), glossopharygeal (IX), and vagus (X) nerves arise in the medulla oblongata.

1. _____

2. _____

3. _____

4. _____

5. _____

6. _____

7. _____

19. _____

18. _____

17. _____

16. _____

15. _____

14. _____

13. _____

12. _____

11. _____

10. _____

9. _____

8. _____

Brainstem – posterior view

20. _____

21. _____

22. _____

23. _____

24. _____

25. _____

26. _____

27. _____

28. _____

29. _____

30. _____

31. _____

39. _____

38. _____

37. _____

36. _____

35. _____

34. _____

33. _____

32. _____

Brainstem – lateral view

Answers

Spinal Cord

In an adult, the spinal cord extends from the base of the skull to a point about two-thirds of the way down the back, running through the vertebral canal. The cord itself has a central region of grey matter, which is divided into posterior (dorsal) and anterior (ventral) horns, and an intermediate zone. The grey matter is surrounded by white matter carrying ascending and descending fibre tracts. The dorsal horns are specialised to relay information up to the brain. The ventral horns contain motor neurons, which transmit messages out to the muscles via spinal nerves. The intermediate zone contains many interneurons involved in linking incoming sensory neurons with outgoing motor neurons to bring about automated (reflex) responses that do not involve the brain. The spinal cord has 31 pairs of nerves arising from it.

16. _____

15. _____

1. _____

14. _____

2. _____

13. _____

3. _____

4. _____

5. _____

6. _____

7. _____

8. _____

9. _____

10. _____

11. _____

12. _____

Spinal Cord – cross-sectional view

Answers

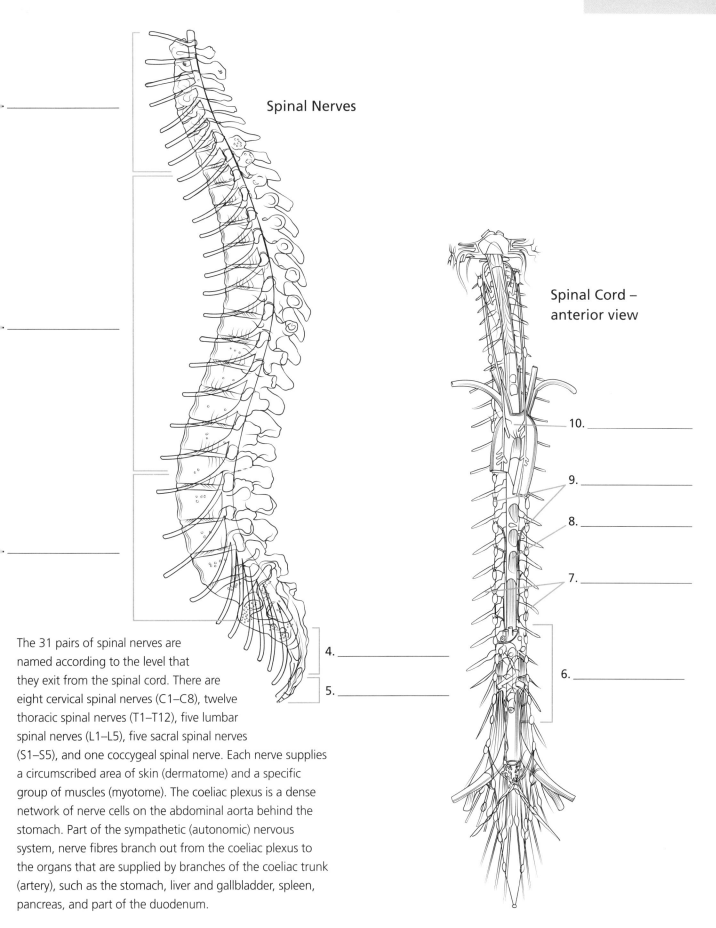

Spinal Nerves

Spinal Cord –
anterior view

10. _____

9. _____

8. _____

7. _____

6. _____

4. _____

5. _____

The 31 pairs of spinal nerves are named according to the level that they exit from the spinal cord. There are eight cervical spinal nerves (C1–C8), twelve thoracic spinal nerves (T1–T12), five lumbar spinal nerves (L1–L5), five sacral spinal nerves (S1–S5), and one coccygeal spinal nerve. Each nerve supplies a circumscribed area of skin (dermatome) and a specific group of muscles (myotome). The coeliac plexus is a dense network of nerve cells on the abdominal aorta behind the stomach. Part of the sympathetic (autonomic) nervous system, nerve fibres branch out from the coeliac plexus to the organs that are supplied by branches of the coeliac trunk (artery), such as the stomach, liver and gallbladder, spleen, pancreas, and part of the duodenum.

Answers

1. Spinal nerves C1–C8, 2. Spinal nerves T1–T12, 3. Spinal nerves L1–L5, 4. Coccygeal spinal nerve, 5. Spinal nerves S1–S5, 6. Coeliac and superior mesenteric plexuses and ganglia, 7. Peripheral nerves, 8. Spinal cord, 9. Sympathetic trunk ganglia, 10. Aortic arch

Dermatomes

Dermatomes are the areas of skin supplied by a single spinal nerve; however, there is usually some overlap between adjacent dermatomes. Each of the 31 segments of the spinal cord gives rise to a pair of spinal nerves, which carry sensory messages into and motor messages out of the central nervous system. These spinal nerves branch into and service particular areas of the body. Spinal nerve C1 does not play a role in dermatomes. The skin of the face is supplied by branches of the trigeminal nerve (cranial nerves V1, V2, and V3).

Dermatomes – lateral view

1. _____
2. _____
3. _____
4. _____
5. _____
6. _____
7. _____
8. _____
9. _____
10. _____
11. _____
12. _____
13. _____
14. _____
15. _____
16. _____
17. _____
18. _____
19. _____

40. _____
39. _____
38. _____
37. _____
36. _____
35. _____
34. _____
33. _____
32. _____
31. _____
30. _____
29. _____
28. _____
27. _____
26. _____
25. _____
24. _____
23. _____
22. _____
21. _____
20. _____

Answers

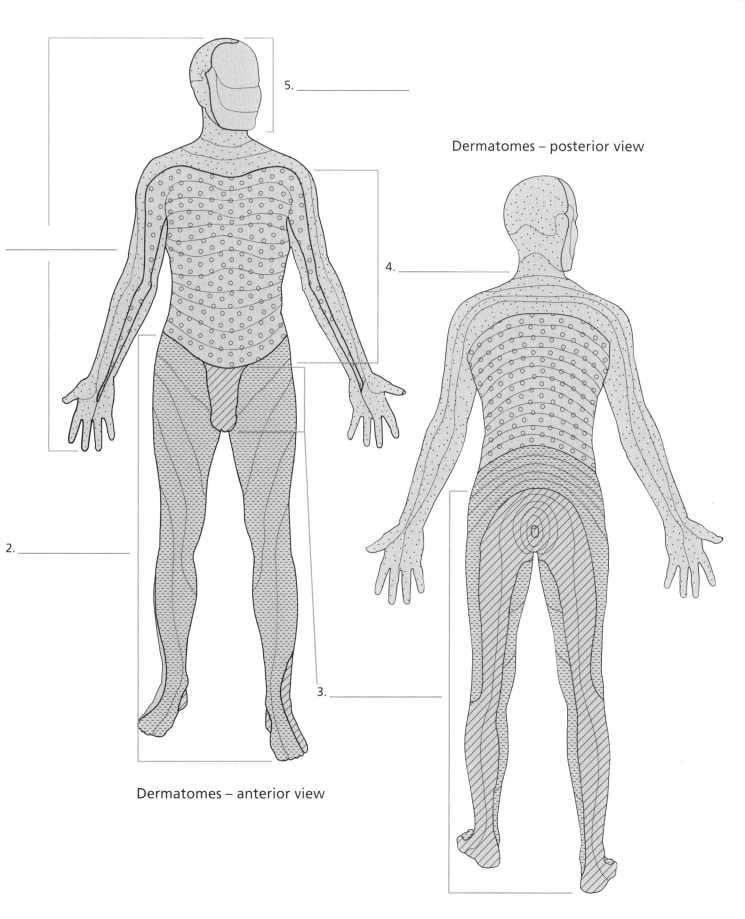

5. _____

Dermatomes – posterior view

4. _____

2. _____

3. _____

Dermatomes – anterior view

Answers

Nerves of the Head and Neck

1. _____

2. _____

3. _____

4. _____

5. _____

8. _____

7. _____

6. _____

Central Nervous System:
Head and Neck Region –
sagittal view

The head contains the brain, encased in the cranium of the skull. The spinal cord in the neck region gives rise to nerves (cervical nerves C1–C8) that pass to the skin and muscles of the neck and upper limbs. They emerge from the spinal cord through openings between the vertebrae (intervertebral foramina). The phrenic nerve, which supplies the diaphragm, arises from the spinal cord in the neck (C3–5 segments). The skull has air cavities (sinuses) that decrease the density of the skull, making it easier to support the head.

Answers

**Nerves of the
Head and Neck –
lateral view**

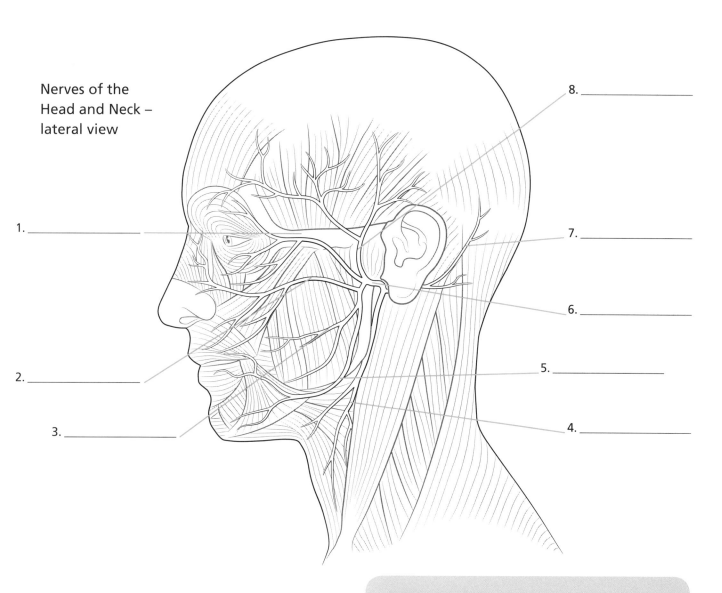

1. _____

2. _____

3. _____

8. _____

7. _____

6. _____

5. _____

4. _____

The facial nerves (cranial nerve VII), one on either side of the face, are the nerves that control the muscles of the face. They also supply the submandibular and sublingual salivary glands in the mouth and the lacrimal glands in the orbit, and carry taste sensation from the front two-thirds of the tongue. The facial nerves emerge from the brainstem, pass through the temporal bone in the skull, exit the skull through the stylomastoid foramen, and then fan out over each side of the face anterior to the ears.

Bell's palsy

The facial nerve passes through a narrow channel in the temporal bone called the facial canal. If the tissues in the canal become inflamed as a result of a viral infection, the subsequent rise in pressure may damage the facial nerve axons – a condition called Bell's palsy. The patient will suffer a paralysis of the muscles controlling facial expression and be unable to smile on the affected side. If the condition affects parasympathetic axons, the patient may also lose control of the lacrimal, submandibular, and sublingual glands. The condition often resolves when the damaged axons recover or regrow.

Answers

1. Zygomatic branch of facial nerve, 2. Upper buccal branch of facial nerve, 3. Lower buccal branch of facial nerve, 4. Cervical branch of facial nerve, 5. Mandibular branch of facial nerve, 6. Trunk of facial nerve, 7. Posterior auricular nerve, 8. Temporal branch of facial nerve

Major Nerves of the Upper and Lower Limbs

The major nerves serving the upper limb are the ulnar nerve, the radial nerve, and the median musculocutaneous nerve. These nerves arise at the brachial plexus in the shoulder region. The ulnar nerve innervates the flexor carpi ulnaris muscle, half of the flexor digitorum profundus muscle, and small muscles of the hand. It provides sensation to the skin on the palm side of the little finger side of the hand. The radial nerve innervates the extensor muscles in the back of the arm and supplies the skin over the back of the arm and hand on the thumb side. The median nerve innervates some of the flexor muscles of the forearm, some of the muscles of the thumb, and some of the skin on the front of the hand. The musculocutaneous nerve innervates the flexor muscles of the arm.

Major Nerves of the Upper Limb – posterior view

9. _____

1. _____

2. _____

3. _____

4. _____

8. _____

7. _____

5. _____

6. _____

Major Nerves of the Wrist – palmar view

10. _____

11. _____

12. _____

13. _____

14. _____

15. _____

Major Nerves of the Upper Limb – anterior view

Answers

1. Radial nerve. 2. Median nerve. 3. Ulnar nerve. 4. Musculocutaneous nerve. 5. Anterior interosseous nerve. 6. Digital nerves of radial nerve. 7. Superficial branch of radial nerve. 8. Deep branch of radial nerve. 9. Axillary nerve. 10. Common palmar digital branches of median nerve. 11. Superficial branch of ulnar nerve. 12. Flexor retinaculum. 13. Median nerve. 14. Superficial branch of radial nerve. 15. Ulnar nerve

Major Nerves of the Lower Limb – anterior view

The femoral nerve, the obturator nerve, and the sciatic nerve are the principal nerves of the lower limb, supplying the muscles and much of the skin. The femoral and obturator nerves arise at the lumbar plexus, and the sciatic nerve arises at the sacral plexus. The sciatic nerve and its branches (the tibial and common fibular nerves) supply the hamstring muscles of the thigh and all the muscles of the leg and foot. The obturator nerve supplies the gracilis muscle and the adductor muscles of the thigh and the skin on the medial part of the thigh. The femoral nerve and its major cutaneous branch, the saphenous nerve, supply the muscles at the front of the thigh, the joints of the hip and knee, and the skin of the thigh, leg, and foot.

1. _____

2. _____

3. _____

4. _____

15. _____

14. _____

5. _____

13. _____

6. _____

7. _____

8. _____

12. _____

11. _____

10. _____

9. _____

Major Nerves of the Lower Limb – posterior view

Answers

1. Lateral femoral cutaneous nerve, 2. Femoral nerve, 3. Obturator nerve, 4. Sciatic nerve, 5. Saphenous nerve, 6. Common fibular nerve, 7. Superficial fibular nerve, 8. Deep fibular nerve, 9. Lateral plantar nerve, 10. Medial plantar nerve, 11. Lateral sural cutaneous nerve, 12. Medial sural cutaneous nerve, 13. Tibial nerve, 14. Branches from femoral nerve, 15. Posterior femoral cutaneous nerve

Autonomic Nervous System

Autonomic Nervous System: Sympathetic Division

1. _____

2. _____

3. _____

4. _____

5. _____

6. _____

7. _____

8. _____

9. _____

10. _____

11. _____

12. _____

13. _____

The autonomic nervous system is the part of the nervous system concerned with controlling relatively automatic body functions. It is divided into sympathetic and parasympathetic divisions. Often referred to as the 'fight-or-flight' system, the sympathetic division comes into play during emergency situations. In such situations, the sympathetic division reacts by increasing heart rate, blood pressure, and blood sugar levels; the pupils dilate; the breathing becomes more rapid; and blood flow to the muscles is increased. The sympathetic division also has an important effect on the control of body temperature and on the urinary and reproductive organs.

Answers

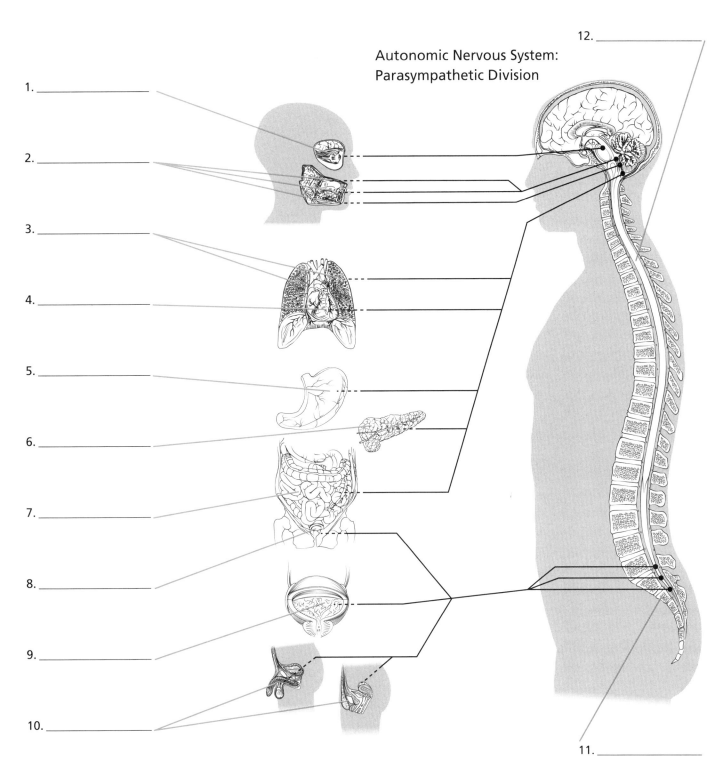

Autonomic Nervous System:
Parasympathetic Division

1. _____

2. _____

3. _____

4. _____

5. _____

6. _____

7. _____

8. _____

9. _____

10. _____

11. _____

12. _____

The pelvic organs and tissues are influenced by both the sympathetic and parasympathetic divisions of the autonomic nervous system. The parasympathetic division is most active when the body is not under threat and when the person is largely at rest. Its main function is to conserve energy, restoring the internal body state to normal by promoting digestion, and eliminating waste products from the body. This involves, for example, increased activity of the salivary glands and the smooth muscle and glands in the stomach and intestines, and lowering of the heart rate and blood pressure.

Answers

1. Eye and lacrimal glands, 2. Salivary glands, 3. Lungs, 4. Heart, 5. Stomach, 6. Pancreas, 7. Small intestine, 8. Rectum, 9. Bladder, 10. Reproductive organs, 11. Sacrum, 12. Spinal cord

Sight

Eye – anterior view

1. _____

2. _____

3. _____

4. _____

5. _____

6. _____

7. _____

8. _____

9. _____

10. _____

11. _____

12. _____

The eye is the organ of sight. Light rays entering the eye strike the cornea, which refracts the rays, bringing them closer together. The rays then pass through the lens, which focuses them on the back of the retina. The retina consists of a layer of light-sensitive cells – rods and cones. When stimulated by light, the rods and cones send electrical signals along the cells of the optic nerve. The optic nerve connects the eye to the brain. The impulses travel via the optic nerves to the occipital cortex and other parts of the brain, where they are interpreted as vision. The eyelids (palpebrae) protect the eyes. Each eyelid is covered on the outside by the skin and on the inside by the conjunctiva. The eyelid margin is lined with a few rows of eyelashes (cilia) and has openings for numerous glands.

13. _____

14. _____

15. _____

16. _____

Eyeball in situ – lateral view

17. _____

18. _____

Answers

Eye – lateral view

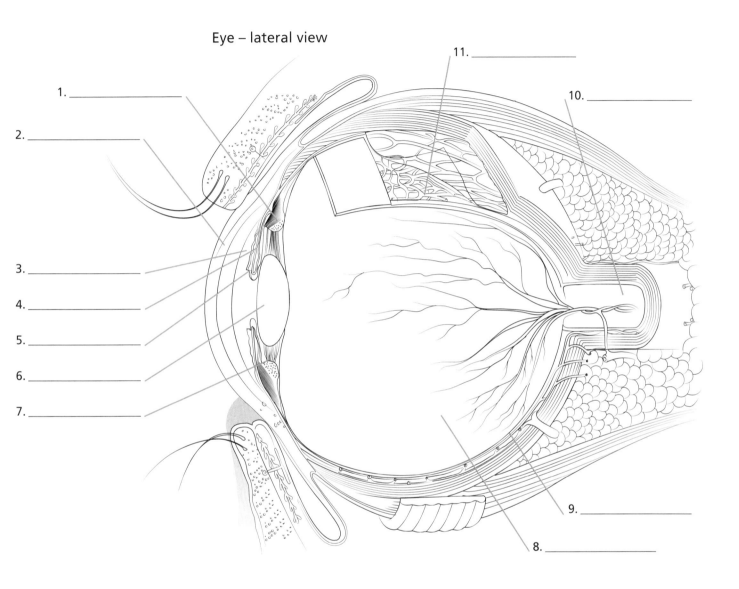

1. _____
2. _____
3. _____
4. _____
5. _____
6. _____
7. _____
8. _____
9. _____
10. _____
11. _____

The eyeball has three layers: the sclera and cornea comprise the outer layer, the uvea and lens comprise the middle layer, and the retina is the inner layer. The sclera gives the eyeball its spherical shape, with the front of the sphere covered by the curved layer of the transparent cornea. The front of the sclera is covered by a thin membrane called the conjunctiva. The uvea has three parts: the choroid, ciliary body, and iris. The choroid is the posterior part of the uvea, the ciliary body contains muscles, and the iris is the anterior part, lying behind the cornea. The retina lines the inside of the back part of the eyeball. The nerve fibres from the retina converge at the optic nerve. The eyeball is divided into two fluid-filled cavities. The anterior cavity is in front of the lens and is made up of the anterior and posterior chambers on the front and posterior sides of the iris, respectively. The anterior cavity contains aqueous humour, and the posterior cavity contains the vitreous body (a gelatin-like mass).

Answers

1. Ciliary body, 2. Cornea, 3. Anterior chamber (of anterior cavity), 4. Posterior chamber (of anterior cavity), 5. Iris, 6. Lens, 7. Ciliary fibres, 8. Vitreous body (of posterior cavity), 9. Retina, 10. Optic nerve, 11. Choroid

Hearing and Balance

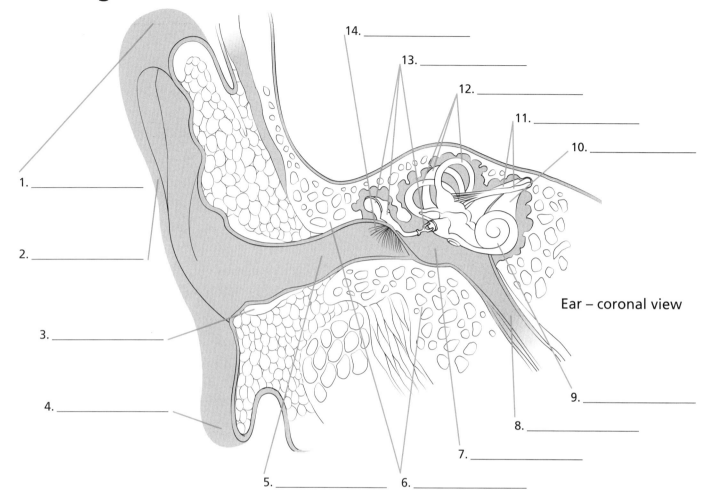

14. _____

13. _____

12. _____

11. _____

10. _____

1. _____

2. _____

3. _____

4. _____

Ear – coronal view

9. _____

8. _____

7. _____

5. _____   6. _____

Sound is conducted to the brain through the ear, the organ of hearing. The outer ear acts as a funnel to collect sound waves and guide them to the tympanic membrane. When sound waves strike the tympanic membrane, they cause it to vibrate and pass vibrations to the ossicles in the middle ear. The ossicles transmit vibrations into the cochlea. There they disturb the cochlear fluid, exciting tiny hair cells in the organ of Corti that send nerve impulses along the cochlear branch of the vestibulocochlear nerve to the hearing centre in the temporal lobe of the brain, where sounds are interpreted. The ear is also the organ of balance; head movements are detected deep inside the inner ear by the semicircular ducts.

Tympanic Membrane (eardrum) – internal view

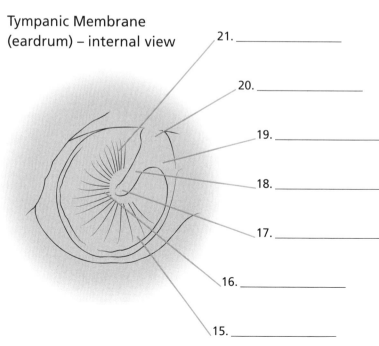

21. _____

20. _____

19. _____

18. _____

17. _____

16. _____

15. _____

Answers

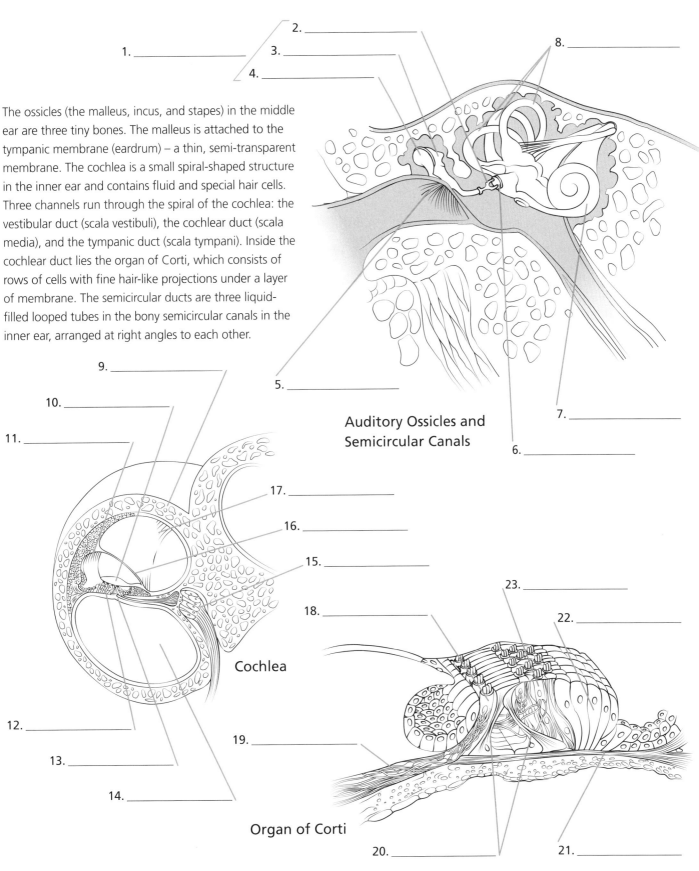

The ossicles (the malleus, incus, and stapes) in the middle ear are three tiny bones. The malleus is attached to the tympanic membrane (eardrum) – a thin, semi-transparent membrane. The cochlea is a small spiral-shaped structure in the inner ear and contains fluid and special hair cells. Three channels run through the spiral of the cochlea: the vestibular duct (scala vestibuli), the cochlear duct (scala media), and the tympanic duct (scala tympani). Inside the cochlear duct lies the organ of Corti, which consists of rows of cells with fine hair-like projections under a layer of membrane. The semicircular ducts are three liquid-filled looped tubes in the bony semicircular canals in the inner ear, arranged at right angles to each other.

1. _____
2. _____
3. _____
4. _____
5. _____
6. _____
7. _____
8. _____

Auditory Ossicles and Semicircular Canals

9. _____
10. _____
11. _____
12. _____
13. _____
14. _____
15. _____
16. _____
17. _____

Cochlea

18. _____
19. _____
20. _____
21. _____
22. _____
23. _____

Organ of Corti

Answers

1. Ossicles, 2. Stapes, 3. Incus, 4. Malleus, 5. Eardrum, 6. Stapes footplate covering vestibular (oval) window, 7. Cochlea, 8. Semicircular canals, 9. Bony cochlear wall, 10. Tectorial membrane, 11. Cochlear duct (scala media), 12. Organ of Corti, 13. Basilar membrane, 14. Tympanic duct (scala tympani), 15. Cochlear nerve, 16. Vestibular membrane, 17. Vestibular duct (scala vestibuli), 18. Inner hair cell, 19. Nerve fibres, 20. Pillar cells, 21. Basilar membrane, 22. Phalangeal cell, 23. Outer hair cell

Taste and Smell

1. _____

2. _____

3. _____

4. _____

Tongue – taste zones

5. _____

6. _____

7. _____

8. _____

9. _____

10. _____

11. _____

Tongue – cross-sectional view

Loss of taste and smell

The enjoyment of food and drink depends on a combination of both taste and smell. Taste is confined to only five modalities: salty, sour, bitter, sweet, and umami. By contrast, the subtle flavours of food are sensed by olfaction. This requires that volatile compounds (odorants) in the food and drink rise through the oropharynx and nasopharynx to the nasal cavity to be detected by the olfactory epithelium. Loss of taste itself is rare and is usually due to facial nerve damage, whereas loss of the ability to sense the aromas of food is common and often due to inflammation and mucus congestion of the nasal cavity.

Answers

1. Bitter taste zone, 2. Sour taste zone, 3. Salt taste zone, 4. Sweet taste zone, 5. Filiform papilla, 6. Fungiform papilla, 7. Muscular layer, 8. Serous gland (Ebner's gland), 9. Trench, 10. Taste bud, 11. Vallate papilla

1. _____

2. _____

3. _____

4. _____

5. _____

6. _____

7. _____

Tongue –
taste pathways

The organs of taste are the taste buds, specialised receptors made up of small clusters of papillae, which are located on the surface and sides of the tongue, the roof of the mouth, and the entrance to the pharynx. The tongue has three types of papillae: filiform, fungiform, and vallate. There are five distinct tastes registered by taste buds: sweet, salt, sour, bitter, and umami (savoury). Most taste buds at the front of the tongue are most sensitive to sweet and salty foods, most at the sides of the tongue are most sensitive to any sour taste, and bitterness is best registered at the back of the tongue. However, all parts of the tongue have some sensitivity to all types of taste. Taste buds send nerve impulses via the cranial nerves to the medulla in the brainstem. From there, the information passes to the thalamus and on to taste-receiving areas in the parietal lobes of the cerebral cortex, where the taste is identified. The olfactory organs provide information about smell that is helpful in interpreting and appreciating different tastes.

Answers

1. Parietal lobe, 2. Thalamus, 3. Olfactory bulbs, 4. Medulla oblongata, 5. Regions of taste buds, 6. Tongue, 7. Epiglottis

Taste and Smell

1. _____

2. _____

3. _____

4. _____

5. _____

6. _____

7. _____

11. _____

10. _____

9. _____

8. _____

Nose – sagittal view

The olfactory system is concerned with the sense of smell. The receptors for the sense of smell are situated in the olfactory mucosa that line the upper part of the cavities of the nose. A small area (about 5 square centimetres) of mucous membrane (the olfactory epithelium) contains about twenty nerves served by about 100 million olfactory receptor cells. The olfactory nerves pass through foramina in the cribriform plate of the ethmoid bone, terminating in the olfactory bulbs in the brain. The olfactory bulbs are ovoid structures forming forwards extensions of the olfactory area of the brain. Sensations received by the olfactory receptor cells are transmitted to the olfactory bulb and then sent along the olfactory tract to the medial olfactory area or lateral olfactory area in the brain.

Anosmia

The sense of smell requires the transmission of information from the olfactory epithelium at the roof of the nasal cavity to the olfactory bulb. Common temporary causes of the loss of the sense of smell (temporary anosmia) include allergic and viral rhinitis, sinusitis, and influenza. Olfactory receptor neurons can replenish themselves even if the olfactory epithelium is damaged. Permanent causes of anosmia include fractures to the base of the skull (which sever the fine nerve fibres that pass through the bone of the nasal roof), damage to olfactory centres in the temporal lobe, Parkinson's disease, and Alzheimer's disease.

Answers

1. Frontal sinus, 2. Nasal bone, 3. Nasal cartilage, 4. Alar cartilage, 5. Nasal vestibule (nostril), 6. Maxilla (hard palate), 7. Soft palate, 8. Inferior nasal concha, 9. Middle nasal concha, 10. Superior nasal concha, 11. Sphenoidal sinus

1. _____

2. _____

3. _____

4. _____

Olfactory System

5. _____

6. _____

7. _____

8. _____

12. _____

11. _____

10. _____

9. _____

Answers

1. Olfactory centres in the brain (in septal region and temporal lobe), 2. Sphenoid bone, 3. Olfactory receptors, 4. Nasal cavity, 5. Olfactory bulb, 6. Frontal lobe of the brain, 7. Olfactory mucosa, 8. Bowman's gland (olfactory gland), 9. Cilia, 10. Olfactory cell, 11. Cribriform plate of the ethmoid bone, 12. Olfactory tract

Lymphatic System

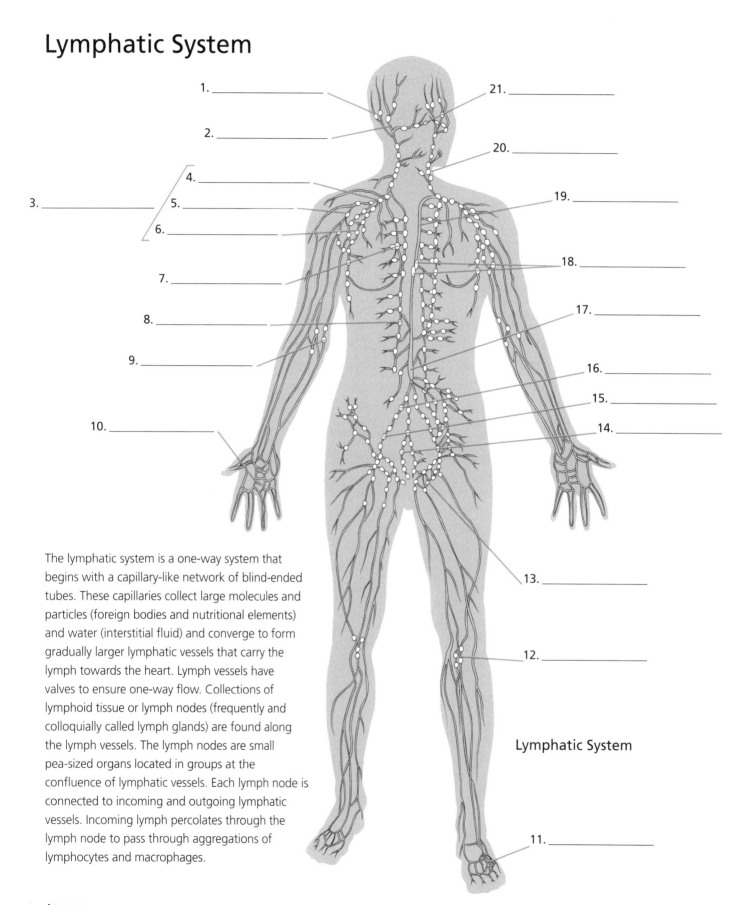

1. _____
2. _____
3. _____
4. _____
5. _____
6. _____
7. _____
8. _____
9. _____
10. _____
11. _____
12. _____
13. _____
14. _____
15. _____
16. _____
17. _____
18. _____
19. _____
20. _____
21. _____

The lymphatic system is a one-way system that begins with a capillary-like network of blind-ended tubes. These capillaries collect large molecules and particles (foreign bodies and nutritional elements) and water (interstitial fluid) and converge to form gradually larger lymphatic vessels that carry the lymph towards the heart. Lymph vessels have valves to ensure one-way flow. Collections of lymphoid tissue or lymph nodes (frequently and colloquially called lymph glands) are found along the lymph vessels. The lymph nodes are small pea-sized organs located in groups at the confluence of lymphatic vessels. Each lymph node is connected to incoming and outgoing lymphatic vessels. Incoming lymph percolates through the lymph node to pass through aggregations of lymphocytes and macrophages.

Lymphatic System

Answers

1. Retroauricular nodes, 2. Parotid nodes, 3. Axillary nodes, 4. Apical axillary nodes, 5. Lateral group, 6. Anterior group, 7. Parasternal nodes, 8. Posterior intercostal nodes, 9. Cubital nodes, 10. Palmar and dorsal plexus, 11. Plantar and dorsal plexus, 12. Popliteal nodes (posterior side of the knee), 13. Inguinal and femoral nodes, 14. Internal iliac nodes, 15. External iliac nodes, 16. Common iliac nodes, 17. Cisterna chyli, 18. Posterior mediastinal nodes, 19. Thoracic duct, 20. Cervical nodes, 21. Buccal nodes

Lymph is a fluid that is filtered and cleaned by white blood cells in the lymph nodes (glands). A lymph node consists of a mass of lymphatic tissue that is surrounded by a fibrous capsule. The nodes cluster in groups along the lymphatic vessels. Each node is enclosed in a fibrous capsule and has compartments divided by partitions of collagen fibres (trabeculae). Each lymph node is connected to incoming and outgoing lymph vessels. Afferent lymphatic vessels bring lymph fluid to the node from surrounding tissues; efferent vessels transport lymph to the veins. Numerous valves prevent the backflow of lymph as it passes through the lymphatic vessels.

1. _____

2. _____

Lymph Vessel

3. _____

4. _____

5. _____

Lymph Node

6. _____

7. _____

13. _____

12. _____

11. _____

10. _____

9. _____

8. _____

Answers

1. Lymphatic endothelial cell, 2. Closed valve, 3. Medullary sinus, 4. Follicle of cortex, 5. Blood capillary, 6. Valve, 7. Efferent lymphatic vessel, 8. Artery, 9. Vein, 10. Subcapsular sinus, 11. Capsule, 12. Trabeculae, 13. Afferent lymphatic vessels

Lymphoid Organs

Lymphoid organs include mucosa-associated lymphoid tissue, the thymus, and the spleen. Concentrations of lymphoid tissue are found in the tonsils and in the gut. The tonsils are arranged around the entrance to the respiratory and digestive tracts to protect the body from bacteria and viruses that may enter from the mouth and nose. The tonsils lie under the surface lining of the mouth and throat and produce lymphocytes that cross into the mouth and throat. There are three sets of tonsils, named according to their positions. The lingual tonsil lies on the back third of the tongue; the palatine tonsils lie on either side of the back of the tongue, between pillars of tissue that join the soft palate to the tongue; and the pharyngeal or nasopharyngeal tonsils (adenoids) lie in the space behind the nose.

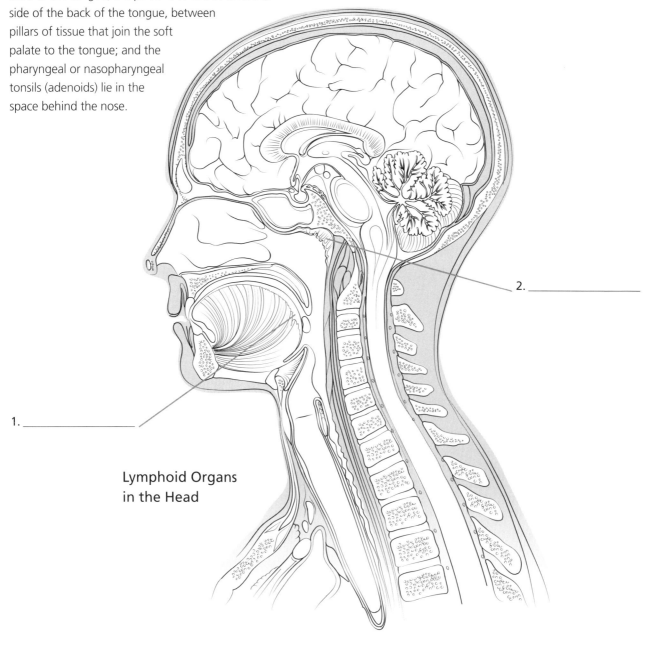

2. _____

1. _____

Lymphoid Organs
in the Head

Answers
1. Lingual tonsil, 2. Pharyngeal tonsil (adenoid)

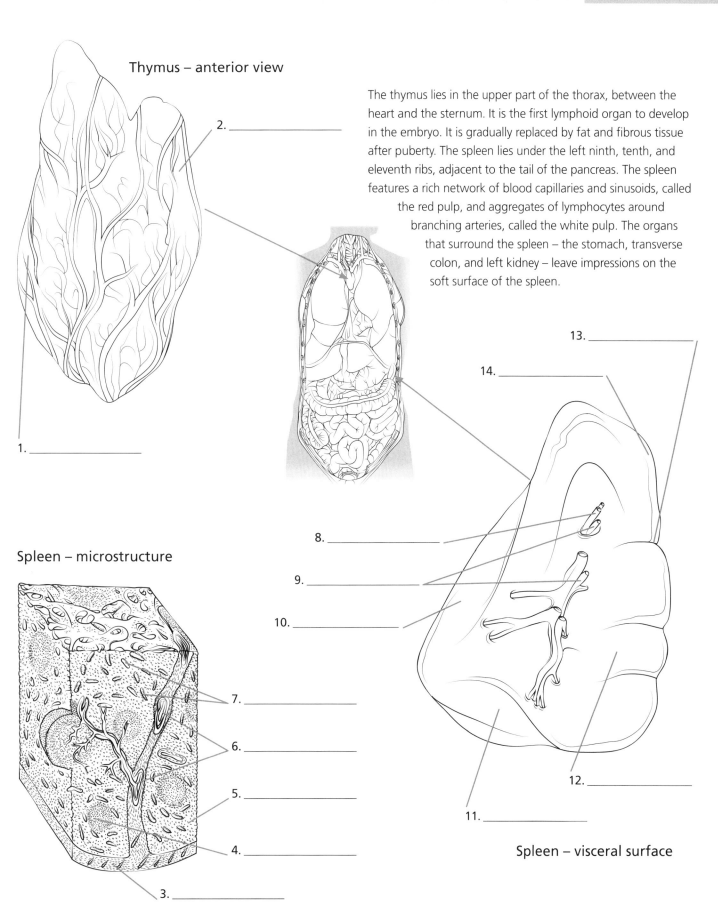

Thymus – anterior view

2. _____

1. _____

The thymus lies in the upper part of the thorax, between the heart and the sternum. It is the first lymphoid organ to develop in the embryo. It is gradually replaced by fat and fibrous tissue after puberty. The spleen lies under the left ninth, tenth, and eleventh ribs, adjacent to the tail of the pancreas. The spleen features a rich network of blood capillaries and sinusoids, called the red pulp, and aggregates of lymphocytes around branching arteries, called the white pulp. The organs that surround the spleen – the stomach, transverse colon, and left kidney – leave impressions on the soft surface of the spleen.

13. _____

14. _____

Spleen – microstructure

7. _____

6. _____

5. _____

4. _____

3. _____

8. _____

9. _____

10. _____

12. _____

11. _____

Spleen – visceral surface

Answers

Circulatory System

Circulatory System – anterior view

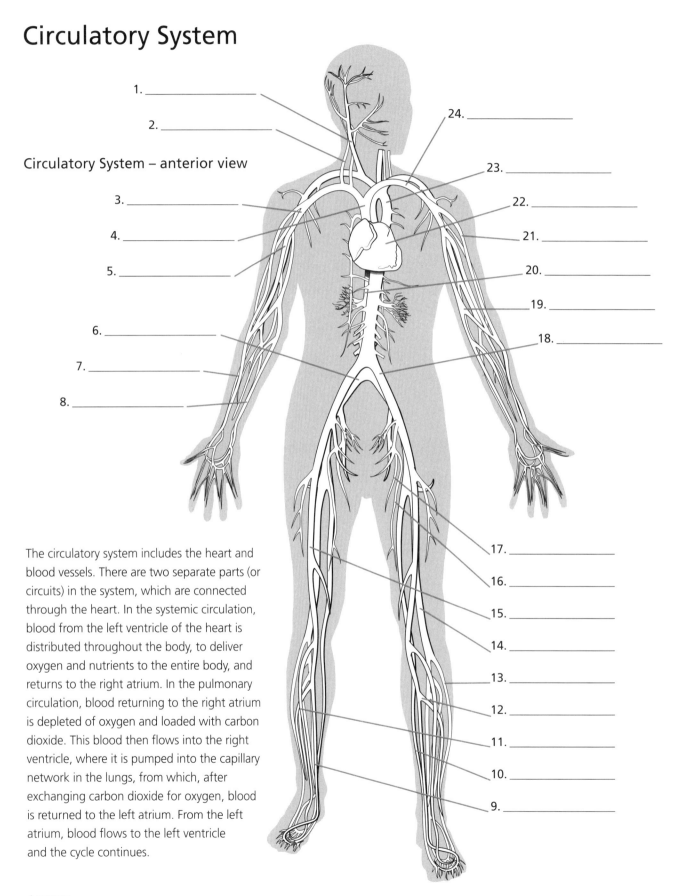

1. _____
2. _____
3. _____
4. _____
5. _____
6. _____
7. _____
8. _____

24. _____
23. _____
22. _____
21. _____
20. _____
19. _____
18. _____
17. _____
16. _____
15. _____
14. _____
13. _____
12. _____
11. _____
10. _____
9. _____

The circulatory system includes the heart and blood vessels. There are two separate parts (or circuits) in the system, which are connected through the heart. In the systemic circulation, blood from the left ventricle of the heart is distributed throughout the body, to deliver oxygen and nutrients to the entire body, and returns to the right atrium. In the pulmonary circulation, blood returning to the right atrium is depleted of oxygen and loaded with carbon dioxide. This blood then flows into the right ventricle, where it is pumped into the capillary network in the lungs, from which, after exchanging carbon dioxide for oxygen, blood is returned to the left atrium. From the left atrium, blood flows to the left ventricle and the cycle continues.

Answers

1. Common carotid artery, 2. External jugular vein, 3. Axillary vein, 4. Superior vena cava, 5. Brachial artery, 6. Common iliac artery, 7. Radial vein, 8. Ulnar artery, 9. Posterior tibial artery, 10. Great saphenous vein, 11. Anterior tibial artery, 12. Fibular artery, 13. Small saphenous vein, 14. Popliteal vein, 15. Femoral artery, 16. Obturator artery, 17. Obturator vein, 18. Common iliac artery, 19. Basilic vein, 20. Inferior vena cava, 21. Cephalic vein, 22. Heart, 23. Arch of aorta, 24. Subclavian vein

Blood – cellular level

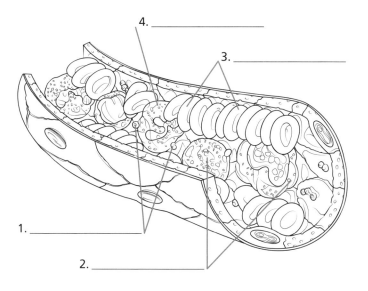

4. _____

3. _____

1. _____

2. _____

Blood is composed of red blood cells (erythrocytes), various types of white blood cells (leukocytes), and platelets in a solution of water, electrolytes, and proteins called plasma. Red blood cells carry oxygen to the tissues, while plasma carries essential nutrients to the tissues. White blood cells are the agents of the body's immune system. Blood vessels form an intricate system through which the blood circulates. As they conduct oxygenated blood away from the heart to the tissues, arteries branch into arterioles, which become capillaries, allowing oxygen and other nutrients to be exchanged in the surrounding tissues. Then, as the capillaries conduct deoxygenated blood back to the heart, they increase in diameter; capillaries become venules, which join to become veins. Many veins contain one-way valves. Fenestrated capillaries have openings, or windows, in their walls; continuous capillaries do not.

Artery

5. _____

6. _____

15. _____

Vein

18. _____

16. _____

17. _____

7. _____

Blood Vessels

11. _____

10. _____

14. _____

8. _____

Capillaries

9. _____

Capillary Bed

12. _____

13. _____

Answers

Circulatory System

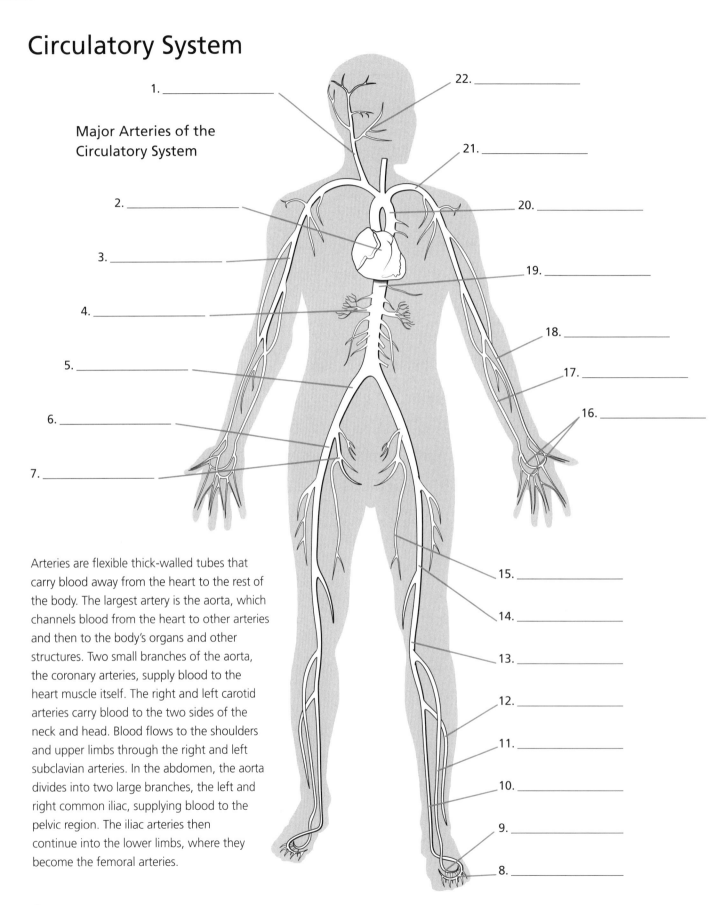

Major Arteries of the Circulatory System

1. _____

2. _____

3. _____

4. _____

5. _____

6. _____

7. _____

22. _____

21. _____

20. _____

19. _____

18. _____

17. _____

16. _____

15. _____

14. _____

13. _____

12. _____

11. _____

10. _____

9. _____

8. _____

Arteries are flexible thick-walled tubes that carry blood away from the heart to the rest of the body. The largest artery is the aorta, which channels blood from the heart to other arteries and then to the body's organs and other structures. Two small branches of the aorta, the coronary arteries, supply blood to the heart muscle itself. The right and left carotid arteries carry blood to the two sides of the neck and head. Blood flows to the shoulders and upper limbs through the right and left subclavian arteries. In the abdomen, the aorta divides into two large branches, the left and right common iliac, supplying blood to the pelvic region. The iliac arteries then continue into the lower limbs, where they become the femoral arteries.

Answers

1. Common carotid artery, 2. Heart, 3. Brachial artery, 4. Renal artery, 5. Common iliac artery, 6. External iliac artery, 7. Internal iliac artery, 8. Arcuate artery, 9. Plantar arch, 10. Posterior tibial artery, 11. Anterior tibial artery, 12. Fibular artery, 13. Popliteal artery, 14. Femoral artery, 15. Obturator artery, 16. Palmar arches, 17. Ulnar artery, 18. Radial artery, 19. Abdominal aorta, 20. Arch of aorta, 21. Axillary artery, 22. Facial artery

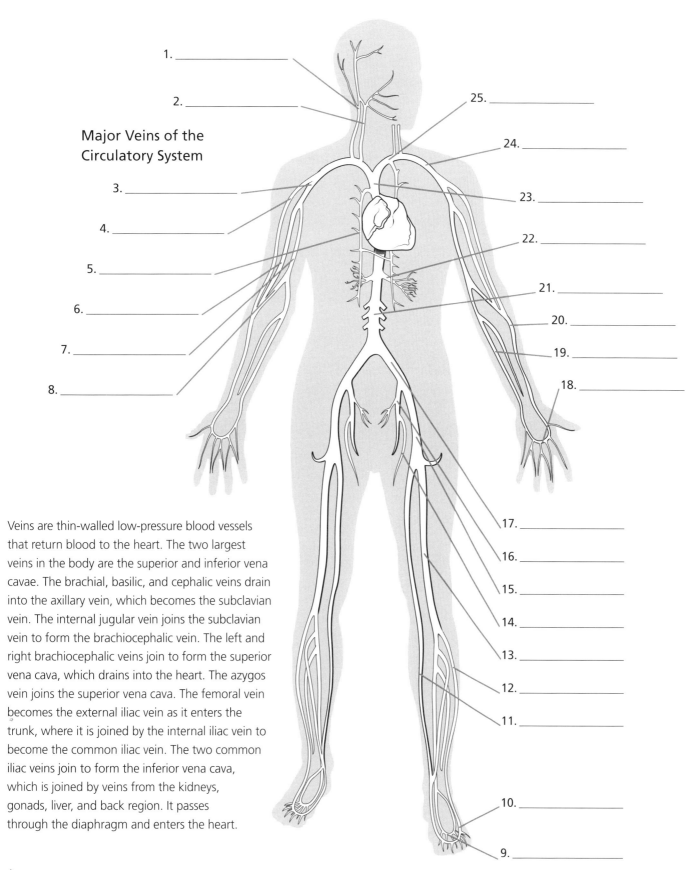

Major Veins of the Circulatory System

1. _____
2. _____
3. _____
4. _____
5. _____
6. _____
7. _____
8. _____
9. _____
10. _____
11. _____
12. _____
13. _____
14. _____
15. _____
16. _____
17. _____
18. _____
19. _____
20. _____
21. _____
22. _____
23. _____
24. _____
25. _____

Veins are thin-walled low-pressure blood vessels that return blood to the heart. The two largest veins in the body are the superior and inferior vena cavae. The brachial, basilic, and cephalic veins drain into the axillary vein, which becomes the subclavian vein. The internal jugular vein joins the subclavian vein to form the brachiocephalic vein. The left and right brachiocephalic veins join to form the superior vena cava, which drains into the heart. The azygos vein joins the superior vena cava. The femoral vein becomes the external iliac vein as it enters the trunk, where it is joined by the internal iliac vein to become the common iliac vein. The two common iliac veins join to form the inferior vena cava, which is joined by veins from the kidneys, gonads, liver, and back region. It passes through the diaphragm and enters the heart.

Answers

1. External jugular vein, 2. Internal jugular vein, 3. Axillary vein, 4. Cephalic vein, 5. Azygos vein, 6. Brachial vein, 7. Basilic vein, 8. Median cubital vein, 9. Plantar venous arch, 10. Dorsal venous arch, 11. Great saphenous vein, 12. Small saphenous vein, 13. Femoral vein, 14. Obturator vein, 15. External iliac vein, 16. Internal iliac vein, 17. Common iliac vein, 18. Palmar venous arch, 19. Ulnar vein, 20. Radial vein, 21. Inferior vena cava, 22. Renal vein, 23. Superior vena cava, 24. Subclavian vein, 25. Brachiocephalic vein

Arteries of the Brain

Cerebral Arteries – inferior view

1. _____

2. _____

3. _____

4. _____

5. _____

6. _____

7. _____

8. _____

9. _____

10. _____

11. _____

12. _____

The brain is supplied by a network of arteries known as the cerebral arteries. The cerebral arteries are formed from the carotid and vertebral arteries. The carotid arteries supply the front (anterior cerebral arteries) and middle (middle cerebral arteries) of the brain; the vertebral arteries supply the back of the brain, cerebellum, and brainstem (posterior cerebral and cerebellar arteries). The three paired cerebral arteries (anterior, middle, and posterior) are joined by communicating arteries (anterior and posterior) to form the cerebral arterial circle (of Willis).

Answers

1. Anterior communicating artery, 2. Internal carotid artery, 3. Posterior cerebral artery, 4. Basilar artery, 5. Anterior inferior cerebellar artery, 6. Posterior inferior cerebellar artery, 7. Vertebral artery, 8. Labyrinthine artery, 9. Superior cerebellar artery, 10. Posterior communicating artery, 11. Middle cerebral artery, 12. Anterior cerebral artery

Cerebral Arteries – sagittal view

1. _____

2. _____

3. _____

4. _____

5. _____

6. _____

7. _____

8. _____

12. _____

11. _____

10. _____

9. _____

Each of the three paired arteries establishes a network of branches that supply blood to various parts of the brain and brainstem. Although the brain makes up only 2 per cent of the average body weight, it uses 20 per cent of the available oxygen.

Berry aneurysms

Congenital weakness in the walls of cerebral arteries can cause ballooning of the vessels at specific points to form berry-shaped aneurysms. These are often found at the branch points of major arteries, for example, the middle cerebral artery, internal carotid artery, and basilar artery. If a berry aneurysm ruptures, blood will rush into the surrounding subarachnoid space (subarachnoid haemorrhage), which can be fatal in about one-third of cases. Berry aneurysms are treated by placing a clip across the base of the aneurysm or by inserting a surgical coil into it to stop blood flow and cause coagulation.

Answers
1. Paracentral artery, 2. Pericallosal artery, 3. Medial frontal branches (of callosomarginal artery), 4. Callosomarginal artery, 5. Polar frontal artery, 6. Medial frontobasal artery, 7. Right anterior cerebral artery, 8. Medial striate artery, 9. Calcarine branch (of medial occipital artery), 10. Parietooccipital branch (of medial occipital artery), 11. Medial occipital artery, 12. Precuneal artery

Blood Vessels of the Head and Neck

1. _____

2. _____

3. _____

Superficial Arteries of the Head and Neck – lateral view

4. _____

5. _____

6. _____

7. _____

8. _____

9. _____

10. _____

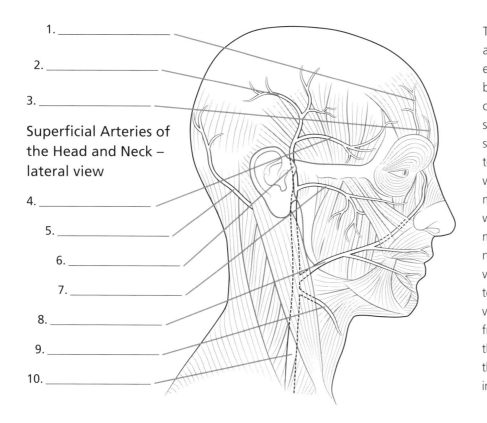

The superficial blood vessels of the head and neck are supplied by branches of the external carotid arteries. Numerous branches lead away from the external carotid artery, supplying blood to the neck, skull, and face. The branches include: the superficial temporal artery, which extends to the top of the head; the facial artery, which extends across the cheek area to the medial side of the eye; the occipital artery, which extends behind the ear; and the maxillary artery, which supplies the jaw, nose, and teeth. The principal superficial veins of the head and neck are the temporal, facial, and occipital veins. These veins drain the superficial area above, in front of, and behind the ear, respectively; the area around the cheeks and nose; and the area around the jaw. These veins drain into the external jugular veins.

11. _____

12. _____

13. _____

Superficial Veins of the Head and Neck – lateral view

14. _____

15. _____

16. _____

17. _____

23. _____

22. _____

21. _____

20. _____

19. _____

18. _____

Answers

1. Supraorbital artery, 2. Posterior branch of superficial temporal artery, 3. Supratrochlear artery, 4. Anterior branch of superficial temporal artery, 5. Occipital artery, 6. Superficial temporal artery, 7. Transverse cervical artery, 8. Facial artery, 9. Transverse cervical artery, 10. External carotid artery, 11. Anterior branch of superficial temporal vein, 12. Supratrochlear vein, 13. Supraorbital vein, 14. Facial vein, 15. Submental vein, 16. Internal jugular vein, 17. Brachiocephalic vein, 18. Subclavian vein, 19. External jugular vein, 20. Retromandibular vein, 21. Posterior auricular vein, 22. Occipital vein, 23. Posterior branch of superficial temporal vein

Blood Vessels of the Eye –
lateral view

8. _____

7. _____

6. _____

5. _____

1. _____

2. _____

3. _____

4. _____

The central artery of the retina enters the eyeball after running
through the centre of the optic nerve. As it emerges from the optic
disc, the central artery of the retina fans out into four main branches
accompanied by their veins. These branches run on the inside of the
retina and spread out into the capillary network. The central vein of
the retina receives blood from the retinal veins. Blood from the
central vein of the retina drains into the superior ophthalmic vein.

Answers

Heart

25. _____

1. _____

24. _____

2. _____

23. _____

3. _____

22. _____

Heart – cross-sectional view

21. _____

20. _____

4. _____

19. _____

5. _____

18. _____

6. _____

17. _____

7. _____

8. _____

16. _____

9. _____

15. _____

10. _____

11. _____

12. _____

13. _____

14. _____

The heart lies in the midline of the thorax, between the lungs, surrounded by the double-layered membrane of the pericardium. The right and left atria are located at the back, and the right and left ventricles at the front. A septum divides the right and left atria and the right and left ventricles. Each atrium opens into a ventricle through an atrioventricular orifice, which is guarded by a valve to ensure that blood flows in only one direction. The left atrium and ventricle are responsible for receiving oxygen-rich blood from the lungs and pumping it out to the body through the aorta. The right atrium and ventricle are responsible for receiving relatively deoxygenated blood from the body and distributing it via the pulmonary trunk to the lungs for gas exchange to occur. A cross-sectional view of the heart exposes the four chambers and valves. The mitral valve sits between the left atrium and ventricle. Blood exiting from the left ventricle is released through the aortic valve. The tricuspid valve sits between the right atrium and ventricle. Blood leaving the right ventricle passes through the pulmonary valve.

Answers

1. Brachiocephalic trunk, 2. Right brachiocephalic vein, 3. Superior vena cava, 4. Ascending aorta, 5. Right pulmonary artery, 6. Right superior pulmonary vein, 7. Right inferior pulmonary vein, 8. Pulmonary valve, 9. Right atrium, 10. Cusp of tricuspid valve, 11. Right ventricle, 12. Papillary muscles, 13. Inferior vena cava, 14. Descending thoracic aorta, 15. Chordae tendineae, 16. Cusp of mitral valve, 17. Left atrium, 18. Left inferior pulmonary vein, 19. Left superior pulmonary vein, 20. Ligamentum arteriosum, 21. Left pulmonary artery, 22. Aortic arch, 23. Left brachiocephalic vein, 24. Left subclavian artery, 25. Left common carotid artery

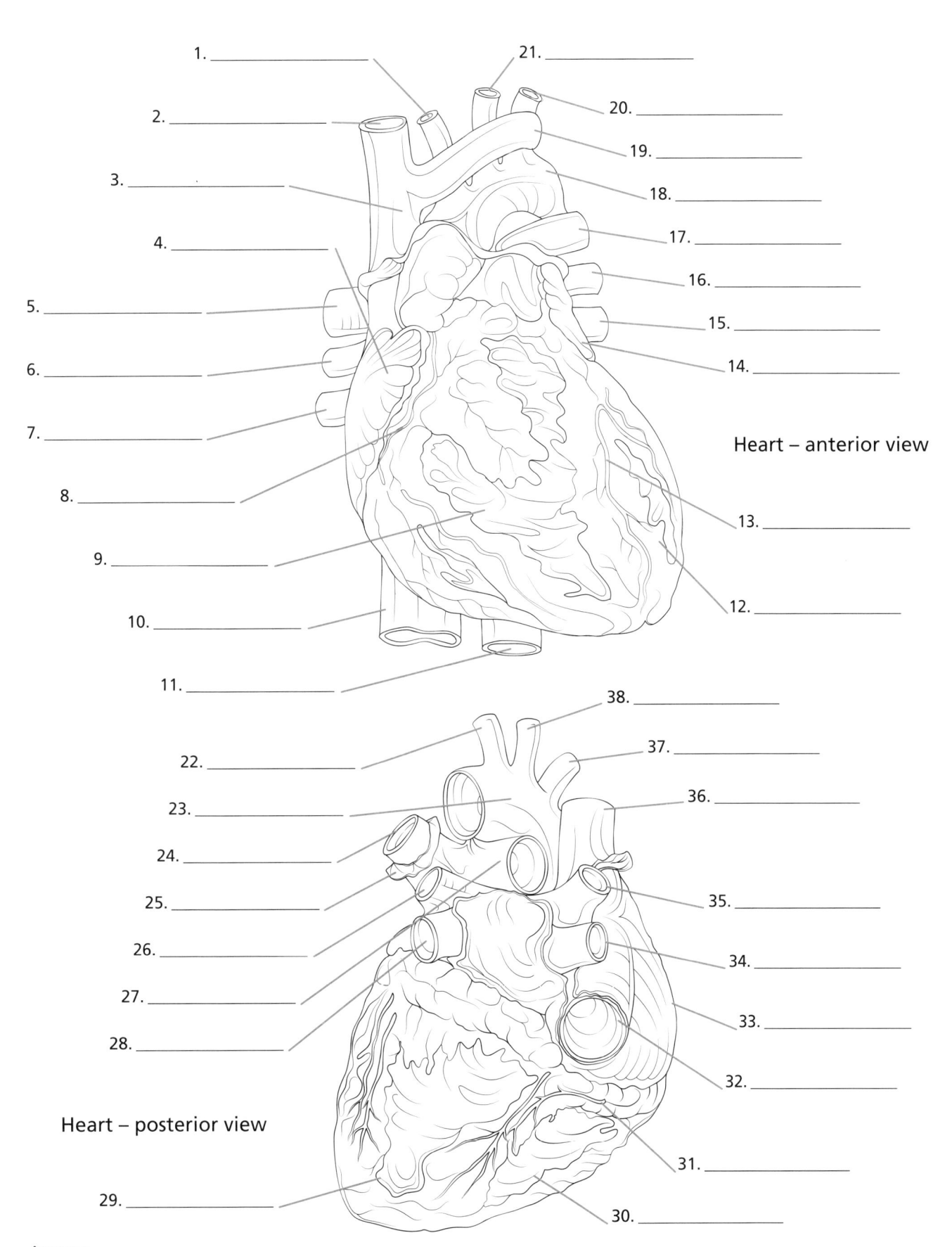

1. _____
2. _____
3. _____
4. _____
5. _____
6. _____
7. _____
8. _____
9. _____
10. _____
11. _____

21. _____
20. _____
19. _____
18. _____
17. _____
16. _____
15. _____
14. _____

Heart – anterior view

13. _____
12. _____

22. _____
23. _____
24. _____
25. _____
26. _____
27. _____
28. _____

38. _____
37. _____
36. _____
35. _____
34. _____
33. _____
32. _____
31. _____
30. _____

Heart – posterior view

29. _____

Answers

1. Brachiocephalic trunk, 2. Right brachiocephalic vein, 3. Superior vena cava, 4. Right atrium, 5. Right pulmonary artery, 6. Right pulmonary artery, 7. Right superior pulmonary vein, 8. Right inferior pulmonary vein, 9. Right ventricle, 10. Inferior vena cava, 11. Descending thoracic aorta, 12. Left ventricle, 13. Anterior descending branch of left coronary artery, 14. Left atrium, 15. Left inferior pulmonary vein, 16. Left superior pulmonary vein, 17. Left pulmonary vein, 18. Aortic arch, 19. Left brachiocephalic vein, 20. Left subclavian artery, 21. Left common carotid artery, 22. Left subclavian artery, 23. Aortic arch, 24. Left pulmonary artery, 25. Pericardium, 26. Left superior pulmonary vein, 27. Right pulmonary vein, 28. Left inferior pulmonary vein, 29. Left ventricle, 30. Right ventricle, 31. Right coronary artery, 32. Inferior vena cava, 33. Right atrium, 34. Right inferior pulmonary vein, 35. Right superior pulmonary vein, 36. Superior vena cava, 37. Brachiocephalic trunk, 38. Left common carotid artery

Heart

Heart Valves: Ventricular Systole

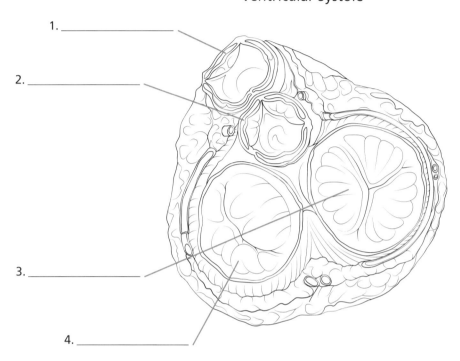

1. _____
2. _____
3. _____
4. _____

The four valves of the heart are designed to allow one-way flow of blood. The atrioventricular valves – the mitral and tricuspid valves – separate the atrium and ventricle on the left and right sides of the heart, respectively. During ventricular systole, the ventricles of the heart contract and the pulmonary and aortic valves open to allow blood to be pumped into the pulmonary and general circulatory systems, respectively, while the mitral and tricuspid valves remain closed. During ventricular diastole, the aortic and pulmonary valves close, while the atrio-ventricular valves (the tricuspid and mitral valves) open to allow blood to pass from the atria to the ventricles. The cusps of the atrioventricular valves have tough fibrous cords, the chordae tendineae, which are attached along the free edge of a valve. The other ends of the chordae tendineae are attached to the papillary muscles.

5. _____
6. _____
7. _____
8. _____
9. _____
10. _____

Heart Valves: Ventricular Diastole

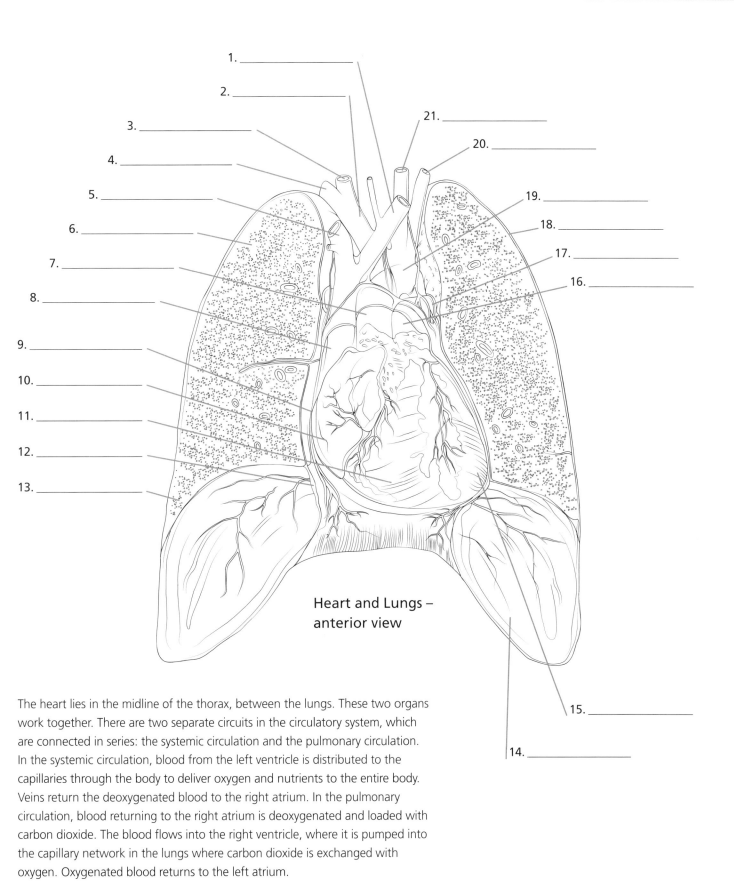

1. _____
2. _____
3. _____
4. _____
5. _____
6. _____
7. _____
8. _____
9. _____
10. _____
11. _____
12. _____
13. _____
14. _____
15. _____
16. _____
17. _____
18. _____
19. _____
20. _____
21. _____

Heart and Lungs –
anterior view

The heart lies in the midline of the thorax, between the lungs. These two organs
work together. There are two separate circuits in the circulatory system, which
are connected in series: the systemic circulation and the pulmonary circulation.
In the systemic circulation, blood from the left ventricle is distributed to the
capillaries through the body to deliver oxygen and nutrients to the entire body.
Veins return the deoxygenated blood to the right atrium. In the pulmonary
circulation, blood returning to the right atrium is deoxygenated and loaded with
carbon dioxide. The blood flows into the right ventricle, where it is pumped into
the capillary network in the lungs where carbon dioxide is exchanged with
oxygen. Oxygenated blood returns to the left atrium.

Answers

1. Left brachiocephalic vein, 2. Brachiocephalic trunk, 3. Right common carotid artery, 4. Right subclavian artery, 5. Right brachiocephalic vein, 6. Right lung (upper lobe),
7. Ascending aorta, 8. Superior vena cava, 9. Pericardium, 10. Right atrium, 11. Right ventricle, 12. Pleura, 13. Right lung (lower lobe), 14. Diaphragm,
15. Left ventricle, 16. Pulmonary trunk, 17. Left pulmonary artery, 18. Left lung (upper lobe), 19. Aortic arch, 20. Left subclavian artery, 21. Left common carotid artery

Blood Vessels of the Abdominal Region

Portal System –
anterior view

1. _____

2. _____

3. _____

4. _____

5. _____

6. _____

7. _____

8. _____

9. _____

10. _____

19. _____

18. _____

17. _____

16. _____

15. _____

14. _____

13. _____

12. _____

11. _____

The portal venous system delivers nutrient-rich blood from the gastrointestinal tract to the liver. Venous blood travels via the splenic vein and the superior and inferior mesenteric veins to the portal vein and thence to the liver. The gastrointestinal tract is supplied by unpaired anterior branches of the abdominal aorta (coeliac trunk and superior and inferior mesenteric arteries). The kidneys, adrenals, gonads, and pelvic organs are supplied by paired lateral branches of the abdominal aorta (the suprarenal, renal, and ovarian or testicular arteries) and iliac vessels.

Answers

1. Inferior vena cava, 2. Liver, 3. Portal vein, 4. Duodenum, 5. Pancreaticoduodenal vein, 6. Superior mesenteric vein, 7. Right colic vein, 8. Appendicular vein, 9. Colon, 10. Rectum, 11. Small intestine, 12. Left colic veins, 13. Inferior mesenteric vein, 14. Pancreas, 15. Splenic vein, 16. Spleen, 17. Left gastric vein, 18. Stomach, 19. Thoracic aorta

17. _____

16. _____

15. _____

14. _____

13. _____

12. _____

11. _____

10. _____

9. _____

8. _____

7. _____

6. _____

1. _____

2. _____

3. _____

4. _____

5. _____

Arterial System
of Abdomen –
anterior view

Answers

Blood Vessels of the Abdominal Region

1. _____

2. _____

3. _____

4. _____

5. _____

6. _____

7. _____

8. _____

9. _____

10. _____

15. _____

14. _____

13. _____

12. _____

11. _____

Renal Arteries (left kidney)

The paired renal arteries branch from the sides of the abdominal aorta. Near each kidney, each renal artery divides into segmental arteries, which enter the hilum of a kidney and divide further before becoming capillaries. Blood to the pelvis is supplied by the right and left internal iliac arteries arising from the respective common iliac arteries. The arrangement of branches is variable, but typically the divisions are posterior (to the pelvic wall structures) and anterior (to the pelvic organs and the gluteal and perineal regions).

Answers

1. Coeliac trunk, 2. Superior mesenteric artery, 3. Segmental artery, 4. Right renal artery, 5. Left renal artery, 6. Left gonadal artery, 7. Right gonadal artery, 8. Ureter, 9. Abdominal aorta, 10. Inferior mesenteric artery, 11. Arcuate artery, 12. Interlobar artery, 13. Renal pyramid (medulla), 14. Cortex, 15. Left adrenal gland

Arteries of the
Pelvic Wall

1. _____

2. _____

3. _____

4. _____

5. _____

6. _____

14. _____

13. _____

12. _____

11. _____

10. _____

9. _____

8. _____

7. _____

Erectile dysfunction

Attaining and maintaining an erection depends on a good flow of arterial blood to the erectile tissues of the penis. Arterial blood flows to the penis through the internal iliac artery and then the pudendal artery. When these arteries are affected by atherosclerosis, their lumens may be narrowed so much that insufficient blood reaches the erectile tissue to raise pressure and cause stiffening. Diabetes mellitus is another common cause of erectile dysfunction. The disease may damage the autonomic nerves that regulate arterial flow (diabetic autonomic neuropathy) so that pelvic arteries cannot be dilated. However, there are medications that can improve blood flow to help sustain an erection.

Answers

1. Common iliac artery, 2. Internal iliac artery, 3. External iliac artery, 4. Obturator artery, 5. Obliterated umbilical artery, 6. Superior vesicle, 7. Uterine artery, 8. Vaginal artery, 9. Middle rectal artery, 10. Internal pudendal artery, 11. Inferior gluteal artery, 12. Superior gluteal artery, 13. Lateral sacral artery, 14. Iliolumbar artery

Blood Vessels of the Upper and Lower Limbs

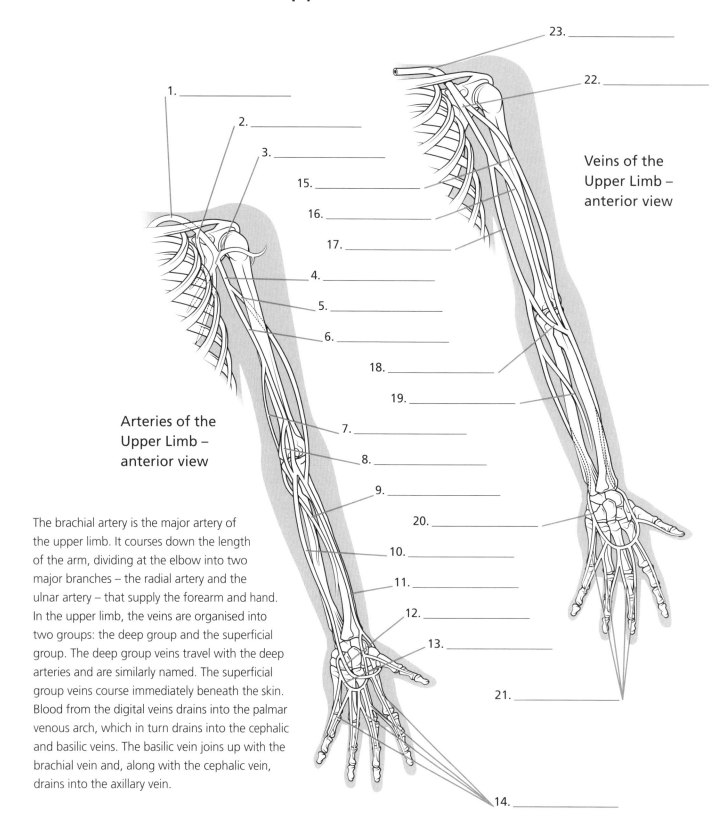

Arteries of the Upper Limb – anterior view

Veins of the Upper Limb – anterior view

1. _____
2. _____
3. _____
15. _____
16. _____
17. _____
4. _____
5. _____
6. _____
18. _____
19. _____
7. _____
8. _____
9. _____
20. _____
10. _____
11. _____
12. _____
13. _____
21. _____
14. _____
22. _____
23. _____

The brachial artery is the major artery of the upper limb. It courses down the length of the arm, dividing at the elbow into two major branches – the radial artery and the ulnar artery – that supply the forearm and hand. In the upper limb, the veins are organised into two groups: the deep group and the superficial group. The deep group veins travel with the deep arteries and are similarly named. The superficial group veins course immediately beneath the skin. Blood from the digital veins drains into the palmar venous arch, which in turn drains into the cephalic and basilic veins. The basilic vein joins up with the brachial vein and, along with the cephalic vein, drains into the axillary vein.

Answers

1. Subclavian artery, 2. Lateral thoracic artery, 3. Subscapular artery, 4. Axillary artery, 5. Deep brachial artery, 6. Brachial artery, 7. Superior ulnar collateral artery, 8. Inferior ulnar collateral artery, 9. Interosseous artery, 10. Ulnar artery, 11. Radial artery, 12. Superficial palmar arch, 13. Deep palmar arch, 14. Digital arteries, 15. Cephalic vein, 16. Brachial vein, 17. Basilic vein, 18. Median cubital vein, 19. Median antebrachial vein, 20. Palmar venous arch, 21. Digital veins, 22. Axillary vein, 23. Subclavian vein

Veins of the Lower Limb – anterior view

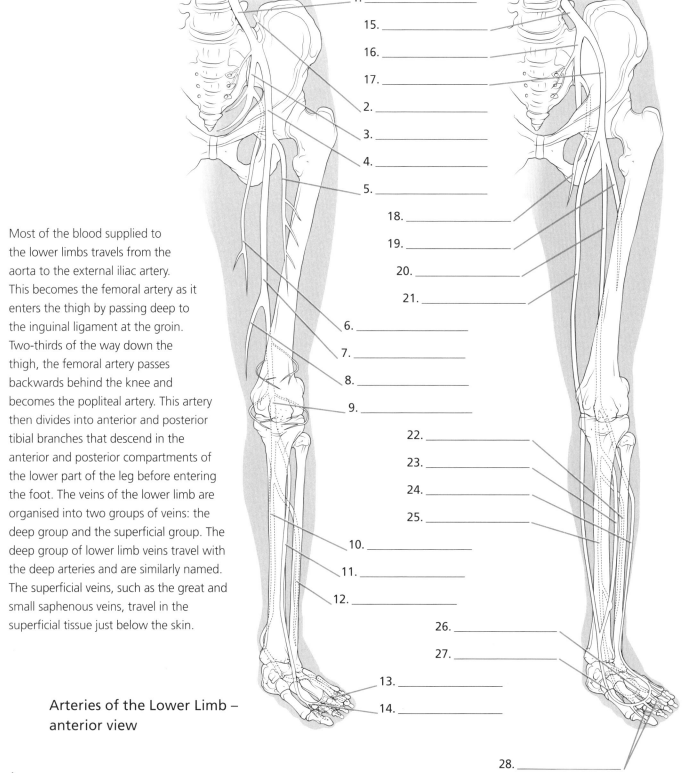

1. _____

15. _____

16. _____

17. _____

2. _____

3. _____

4. _____

5. _____

18. _____

19. _____

20. _____

21. _____

6. _____

7. _____

8. _____

9. _____

22. _____

23. _____

24. _____

25. _____

10. _____

11. _____

12. _____

26. _____

27. _____

13. _____

14. _____

28. _____

Most of the blood supplied to the lower limbs travels from the aorta to the external iliac artery. This becomes the femoral artery as it enters the thigh by passing deep to the inguinal ligament at the groin. Two-thirds of the way down the thigh, the femoral artery passes backwards behind the knee and becomes the popliteal artery. This artery then divides into anterior and posterior tibial branches that descend in the anterior and posterior compartments of the lower part of the leg before entering the foot. The veins of the lower limb are organised into two groups of veins: the deep group and the superficial group. The deep group of lower limb veins travel with the deep arteries and are similarly named. The superficial veins, such as the great and small saphenous veins, travel in the superficial tissue just below the skin.

Arteries of the Lower Limb – anterior view

Answers

1. Common iliac artery, 2. Iliolumbar artery, 3. Internal iliac artery, 4. External iliac artery, 5. Deep femoral artery, 6. Obturator artery, 7. Femoral artery, 8. Descending genicular artery, 9. Popliteal artery, 10. Posterior tibial artery, 11. Anterior tibial artery, 12. Fibular artery, 13. Plantar artery, 14. Arcuate artery, 15. Common iliac vein, 16. Internal iliac vein, 17. External iliac vein, 18. Obturator vein, 19. Profunda femoris vein, 20. Femoral vein, 21. Great saphenous vein, 22. Fibular vein, 23. Anterior tibial vein, 24. Small saphenous vein, 25. Posterior tibial vein, 26. Plantar venous arch, 27. Dorsal venous arch, 28. Digital veins

Respiratory System

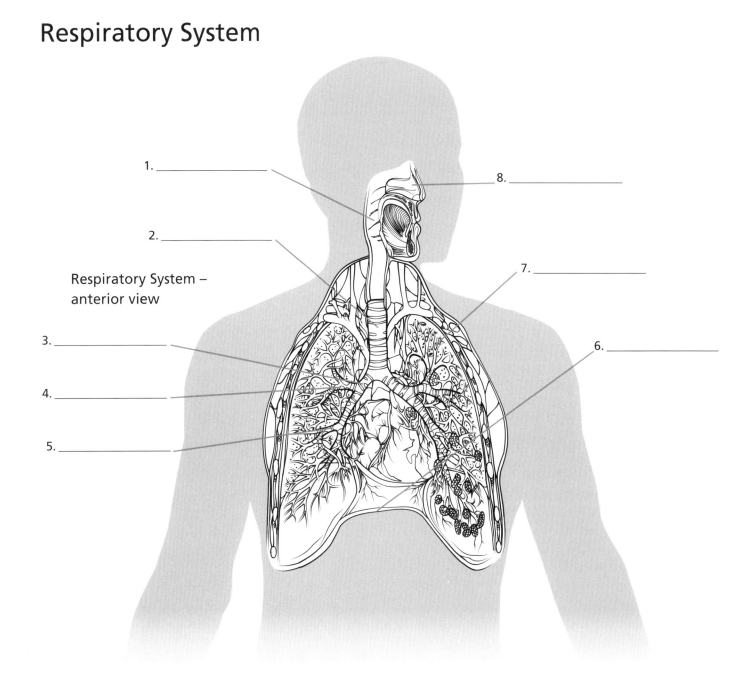

1. _____

2. _____

Respiratory System –
anterior view

3. _____

4. _____

5. _____

8. _____

7. _____

6. _____

In the process of metabolism, the body consumes oxygen and produces carbon dioxide as a waste product. The respiratory system is designed to exchange oxygen in the airways for carbon dioxide accumulated in the blood. Air that is inhaled flows into the airways via the nose, pharynx, larynx, and bronchi. Blood travels continuously through two different circulations: the systemic and the pulmonary circulations. The heart pumps deoxygenated blood from the veins of the systemic circulation into the arteries of the pulmonary circulation. This blood is oxygenated by the lungs and then flows back to the heart to be pumped into the arteries of the systemic circulation.

Answers

1. Pharynx, 2. Trachea, 3. Right primary bronchus, 4. Superior lobar bronchus, 5. Middle lobar bronchus, 6. Diaphragm, 7. Left primary bronchus, 8. Nasal cavity

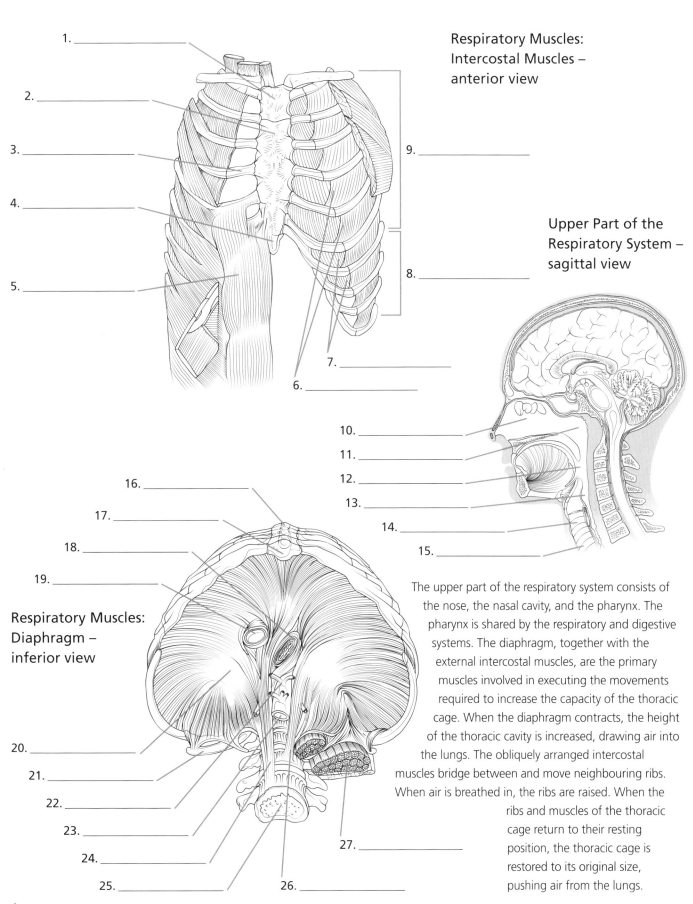

Respiratory Muscles:
Intercostal Muscles –
anterior view

1. _____

2. _____

3. _____

4. _____

5. _____

6. _____

7. _____

8. _____

9. _____

Upper Part of the
Respiratory System –
sagittal view

10. _____

11. _____

12. _____

13. _____

14. _____

15. _____

Respiratory Muscles:
Diaphragm –
inferior view

16. _____

17. _____

18. _____

19. _____

20. _____

21. _____

22. _____

23. _____

24. _____

25. _____

26. _____

27. _____

The upper part of the respiratory system consists of the nose, the nasal cavity, and the pharynx. The pharynx is shared by the respiratory and digestive systems. The diaphragm, together with the external intercostal muscles, are the primary muscles involved in executing the movements required to increase the capacity of the thoracic cage. When the diaphragm contracts, the height of the thoracic cavity is increased, drawing air into the lungs. The obliquely arranged intercostal muscles bridge between and move neighbouring ribs. When air is breathed in, the ribs are raised. When the ribs and muscles of the thoracic cage return to their resting position, the thoracic cage is restored to its original size, pushing air from the lungs.

Answers

1. Manubrium, 2. Body of sternum, 3. Costal cartilage, 4. Xiphoid process, 5. Rectus abdominis muscle, 6. External intercostal muscles, 7. Internal intercostal muscles, 8. Ribs 8–10 ('floating' ribs), 9. Ribs 1–7 ('true' ribs), 10. Nasal cavity, 11. Nasopharynx, 12. Oropharynx, 13. Laryngopharynx, 14. Larynx, 15. Trachea, 16. Body of sternum, 17. Xiphoid process, 18. Oesophagus, 19. Inferior vena cava, 20. Central tendon, 21. Twelfth rib, 22. Coeliac trunk, 23. Abdominal aorta, 24. Right crus of diaphragm, 25. Vertebral column, 26. Left crus of diaphragm, 27. Quadratus lumborum muscle

Nose, Pharynx, and Larynx

Lined with ciliated mucous membrane, the paranasal sinuses are air-containing cavities within the frontal, sphenoid, ethmoid, and maxillary bones of the skull, which are connected by passages to the nose. The paranasal sinuses are rudimentary at birth and develop rapidly at the age of puberty. The lacrimal glands, one above each eye, produce fluid (tears), which moves across the eye from the outer corner towards the nose, lubricating the eyeball. The tears eventually drain into the nose through the nasolacrimal duct and are swallowed or blown out with other nasal fluids.

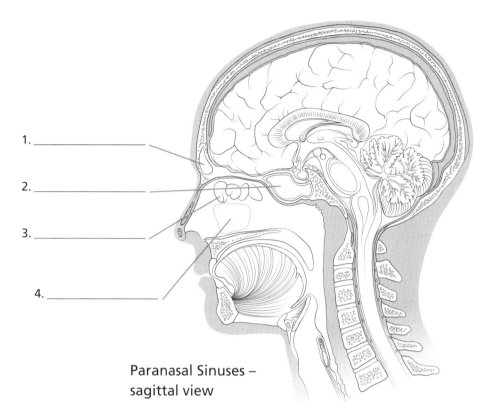

1. _____

2. _____

3. _____

4. _____

Paranasal Sinuses –
sagittal view

5. _____

6. _____

7. _____

Lacrimal Apparatus –
anterior view

Answers

Pharynx – posterior view

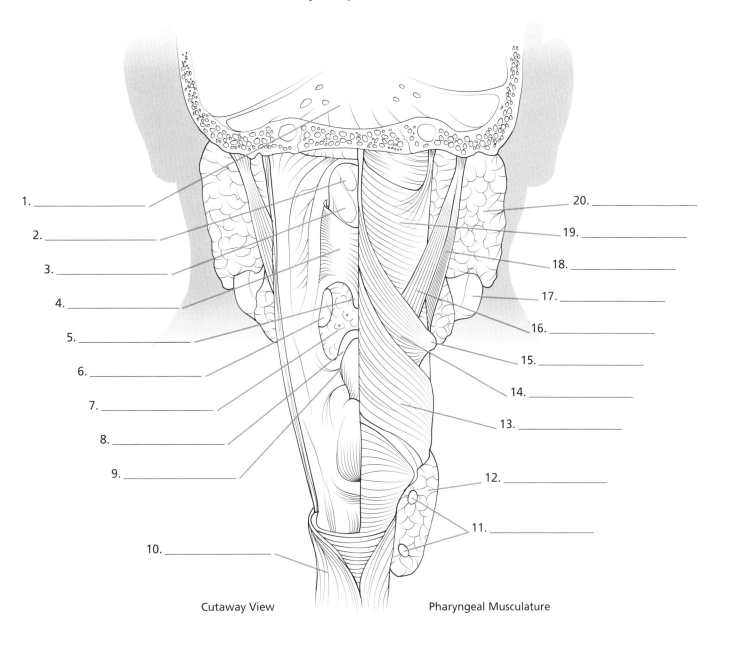

1. _____
2. _____
3. _____
4. _____
5. _____
6. _____
7. _____
8. _____
9. _____
10. _____

11. _____
12. _____
13. _____
14. _____
15. _____
16. _____
17. _____
18. _____
19. _____
20. _____

Cutaway View

Pharyngeal Musculature

The pharynx lies behind the nasal cavity, oral cavity, and larynx and ends in the oesophagus. The pharynx has openings to all these regions and is a common passage for air, liquid, and food. Located on each side wall of the pharynx, just behind the nasal cavity, is the opening of the auditory (Eustachian) tube, which connects the pharynx with the middle ear cavity. The pharynx has three parts: the nasopharynx, oropharynx, and laryngopharynx. The nasopharynx lies immediately beneath the base of the skull and behind the nose. The oropharynx lies behind the mouth. The laryngopharynx, or hypopharynx, is the lowest part of the pharynx and extends from the tip of the epiglottic cartilage to the lower edge of the larynx.

Answers

Nose, Pharynx, and Larynx

The larynx extends from the back of the tongue to the trachea. The larynx is composed of nine cartilages that provide strength for the airway and attachments for the muscles, ligaments, and membranes of the larynx. The upper segment of the larynx commences at the epiglottis and ends at the vestibular folds, or 'false vocal folds' (false vocal cords). The lower segment begins at the true vocal folds (true vocal cords) and ends at the lower border of the cricoid cartilage. The cricoid cartilage, attached to the trachea below, is the only complete ring of cartilage in the respiratory system. The vocal cords are attached to the thyroid cartilage at the front and to the arytenoid cartilages at the back. The thyroid cartilage, which is connected by a membrane to the hyoid bone above and to the cricoid cartilage below, protects the front of the larynx.

Larynx – sagittal view

1. _____
2. _____
3. _____
4. _____
5. _____
6. _____
7. _____
8. _____
9. _____
10. _____
11. _____
12. _____

13. _____
14. _____
15. _____
16. _____
17. _____
18. _____
19. _____
20. _____
21. _____

Larynx – posterior view

25. _____
24. _____
26. _____
27. _____
28. _____
23. _____
22. _____

Larynx – anterior view

Answers

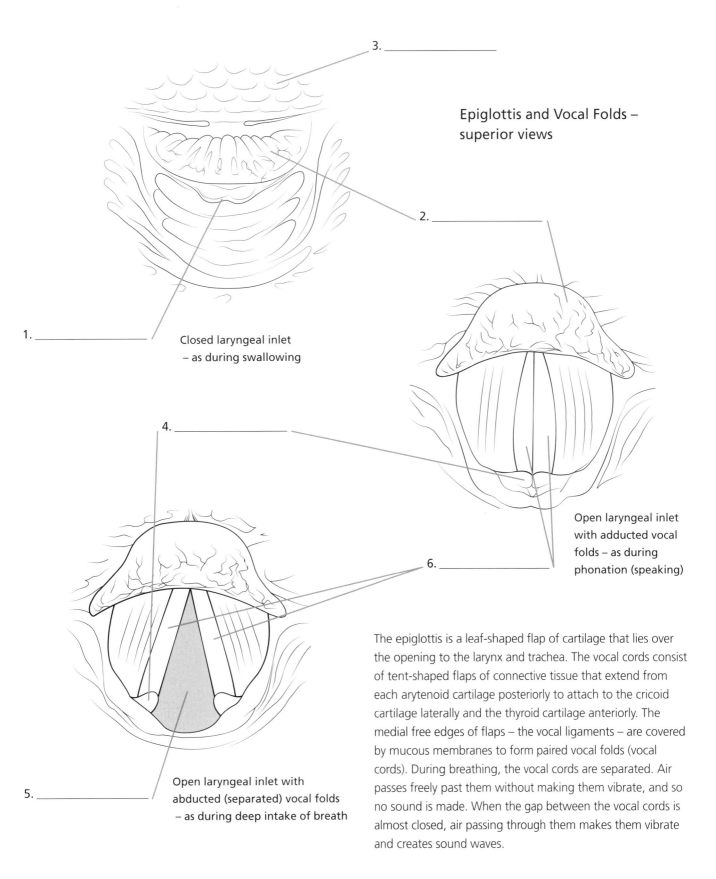

3. _____

Epiglottis and Vocal Folds –
superior views

2. _____

1. _____

Closed laryngeal inlet
– as during swallowing

4. _____

Open laryngeal inlet
with adducted vocal
folds – as during
phonation (speaking)

6. _____

5. _____

Open laryngeal inlet with
abducted (separated) vocal folds
– as during deep intake of breath

The epiglottis is a leaf-shaped flap of cartilage that lies over
the opening to the larynx and trachea. The vocal cords consist
of tent-shaped flaps of connective tissue that extend from
each arytenoid cartilage posteriorly to attach to the cricoid
cartilage laterally and the thyroid cartilage anteriorly. The
medial free edges of flaps – the vocal ligaments – are covered
by mucous membranes to form paired vocal folds (vocal
cords). During breathing, the vocal cords are separated. Air
passes freely past them without making them vibrate, and so
no sound is made. When the gap between the vocal cords is
almost closed, air passing through them makes them vibrate
and creates sound waves.

Answers

1. Corniculate tubercle, 2. Epiglottis, 3. Root of tongue, 4. Vocal process of arytenoid cartilage, 5. Trachea, 6. Vocal folds

Trachea and Bronchi

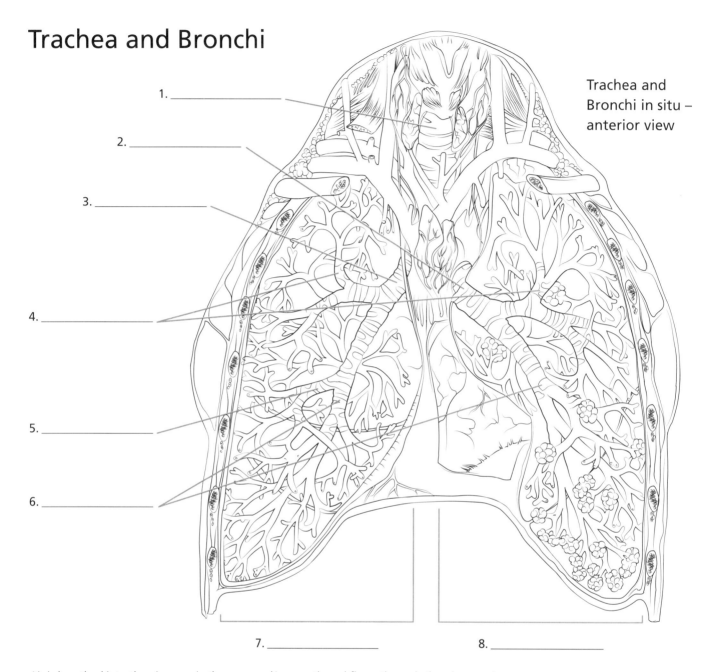

Trachea and Bronchi in situ – anterior view

1. _____

2. _____

3. _____

4. _____

5. _____

6. _____

7. _____

8. _____

Air is breathed into the airways via the nose and/or mouth and flows through the pharynx, larynx, trachea, and bronchi. At its lower end, the trachea branches into the right primary bronchus and the left primary bronchus. Each primary bronchus branches into smaller secondary bronchi at the lung's entrance. Each secondary bronchus divides into smaller tertiary bronchi. These bronchi split into subsequent generations of smaller and smaller bronchi, which finally split into bronchioles that separate into terminal bronchioles. The bronchioles end at the microscopic air sacs (alveoli) where the exchange of carbon dioxide for oxygen occurs. The trachea is reinforced at the front and sides by C-shaped plates of cartilage. Bridging the ends of the cartilage is the trachealis muscle. The internal lining of the trachea is respiratory epithelium. Similar in composition to the trachea, the bronchi and bronchioles feature a muscular exterior lined with respiratory epithelium. Cartilage also forms part of the structure of bronchi, but as the bronchi subdivide the amount of cartilage gradually lessens, and when the bronchioles are reached there is no cartilage present.

Answers

1. Trachea, 2. Left primary bronchus, 3. Right primary bronchus, 4. Superior lobar bronchi, 5. Middle lobar bronchi, 6. Inferior lobar bronchus, 7. Right lung, 8. Left lung

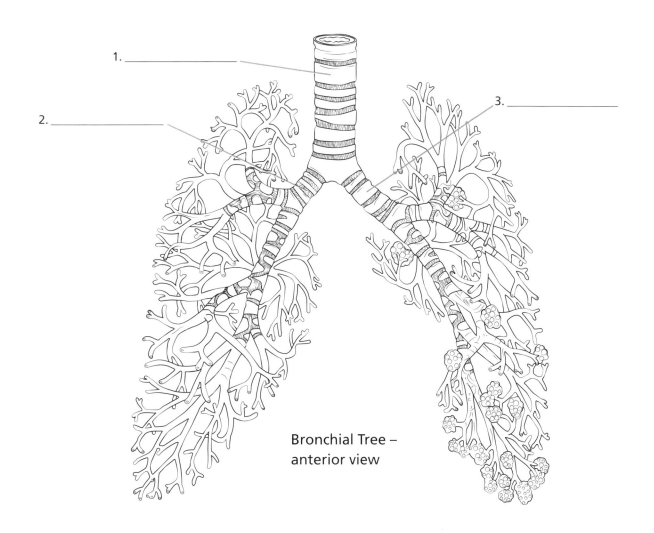

1. _____

2. _____

3. _____

Bronchial Tree –
anterior view

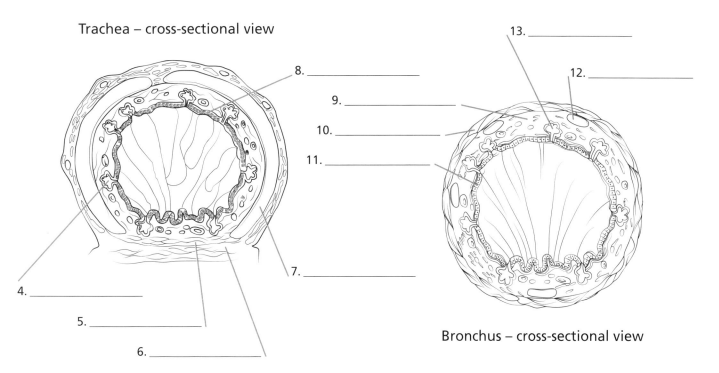

Trachea – cross-sectional view

8. _____

9. _____

10. _____

11. _____

7. _____

4. _____

5. _____

6. _____

13. _____

12. _____

Bronchus – cross-sectional view

Answers

Lungs

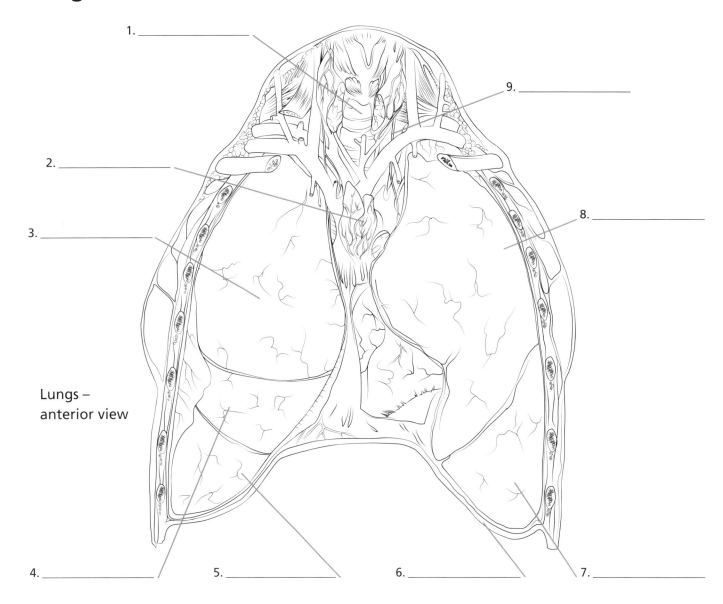

1. _____

9. _____

2. _____

8. _____

3. _____

Lungs – anterior view

4. _____

5. _____

6. _____

7. _____

The lungs are the two main organs of the respiratory system, lying on either side of the heart within the chest cavity. The lungs are enclosed within pleural sacs. Each lung has a roughly conical or pyramidal shape, with a base sitting on top of the diaphragm; sides in contact with the ribcage (costal surface), the mediastinum (mediastinal surface), and the backbone (vertebral surface); and an apex. The lung apex is encircled by the first rib and lies above the first rib in the hollow at the angle between the neck and the shoulder. On the mediastinal surface of each lung is the lung hilum, where the left and right main bronchi enter the lung and the pulmonary arteries and veins enter and exit, respectively. The lungs are divided into lobes – usually three in the right lung and two in the left lung – by a series of clefts or fissures. The mediastinum contains the heart and pericardium, oesophagus, trachea, and associated blood vessels and nerves. The mediastinal organs are encircled by the sternum of the thoracic cage at the front, by the lungs and pleura (pleural cavities) on each side, and by the vertebral column at the back.

Answers

1. Trachea, 2. Thymus gland, 3. Upper lobe (right lung), 4. Middle lobe (right lung), 5. Lower lobe (right lung), 6. Diaphragm, 7. Lower lobe (left lung), 8. Upper lobe (left lung), 9. Cardiac branch of vagus nerve

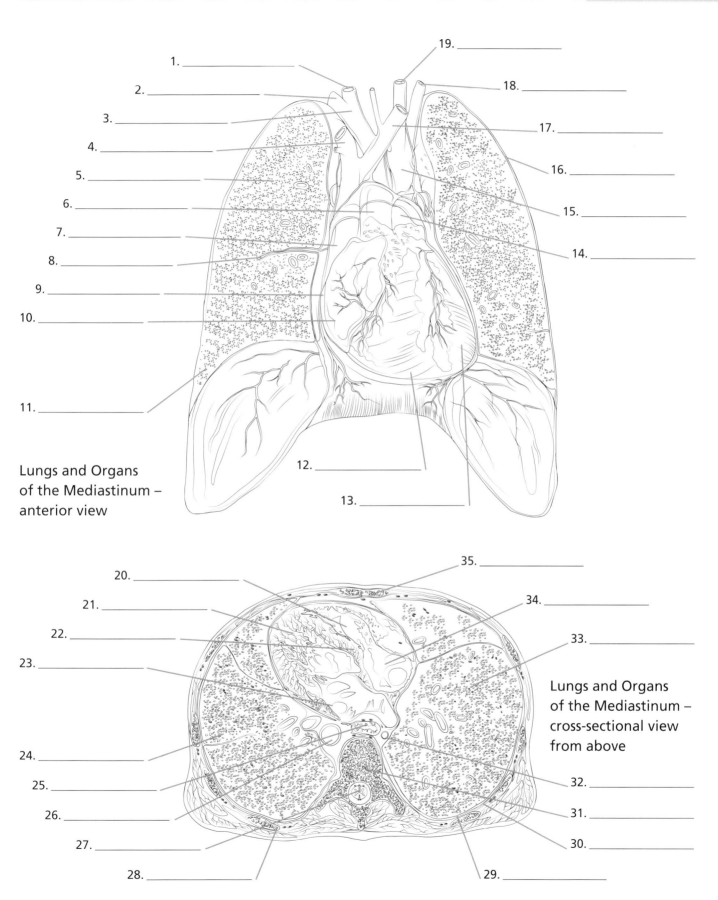

1. _____
2. _____
3. _____
4. _____
5. _____
6. _____
7. _____
8. _____
9. _____
10. _____
11. _____
12. _____
13. _____

14. _____
15. _____
16. _____
17. _____
18. _____
19. _____

Lungs and Organs
of the Mediastinum –
anterior view

20. _____
21. _____
22. _____
23. _____
24. _____
25. _____
26. _____
27. _____
28. _____
29. _____
30. _____
31. _____
32. _____
33. _____
34. _____
35. _____

Lungs and Organs
of the Mediastinum –
cross-sectional view
from above

Answers

Digestive System

Digestive System – anterior view

1. _____

2. _____

3. _____

4. _____

5. _____

6. _____

7. _____

8. _____

9. _____

18. _____

17. _____

16. _____

15. _____

14. _____

13. _____

12. _____

11. _____

10. _____

The digestive tract organs consist of the alimentary tract, which extends from the mouth to the anus, and the accessory organs of the liver, gallbladder, and pancreas. The mechanical action of the digestive tract optimises the chemical actions of enzymes. The entire tract has smooth muscle fibres running in circular and longitudinal directions. The circular fibres contract sequentially along the tract (peristalsis) to knead the contents with digestive enzymes or to move digested food along the tract. The process of digestion breaks down foods into small simple molecules for absorption as energy sources and building blocks for cells.

Answers

1. Tongue, 2. Liver (lifted up), 3. Gallbladder, 4. Duodenum, 5. Pancreas, 6. Ascending colon, 7. Caecum, 8. Appendix, 9. Rectum, 10. Ileum, 11. Descending colon, 12. Jejunum, 13. Transverse colon, 14. Spleen, 15. Pylorus, 16. Stomach, 17. Gastro-oesophageal (cardio-oesophageal) junction, 18. Oesophagus

Upper Part of the Abdomen – transverse section viewed from below

18. _____

17. _____

16. _____

1. _____

2. _____

3. _____

4. _____

5. _____

6. _____

7. _____

15. _____

14. _____

13. _____

12. _____

11. _____

10. _____

9. _____

8. _____

Situated between the thorax and the pelvis, the abdomen is the larger of the body's three major cavities (the other two are the thorax, or chest, and the pelvis). The abdomen contains organs associated with digestion (the stomach, small and large intestines, liver, gallbladder, and pancreas) and urination (kidneys and ureters). These sections through the upper part of the abdomen and the middle part of the abdomen show the relationship and location of the organs and blood vessels found in these different parts of the abdomen. To identify internal organs and for diagnostic purposes, the abdomen is usually divided into four quadrants: right upper, right lower, left upper, and left lower.

30. _____

Middle Part of the Abdomen – transverse section viewed from below

29. _____

28. _____

27. _____

26. _____

25. _____

24. _____

23. _____

19. _____

20. _____

21. _____

22. _____

Answers

1. Bile duct, 2. Portal vein, 3. Inferior vena cava, 4. Liver, 5. Liver, 6. Right crus of diaphragm, 7. Right kidney, 8. Spinal cord, 9. Vertebral body, 10. Perirenal fat, 11. Left kidney, 12. Left crus of diaphragm, 13. Abdominal aorta, 14. Omental bursa, 15. Spleen, 16. Stomach, 17. Lesser omentum, 18. Hepatic artery, 19. Ascending colon, 20. Liver (right lobe), 21. Inferior vena cava, 22. Right kidney, 23. Spinal cord, 24. Vertebra (body and lamina with spine), 25. Left kidney, 26. Abdominal aorta, 27. Spleen, 28. Descending colon, 29. Transverse colon, 30. Loops of small intestine.

Digestive System

The oral cavity includes the mouth and its associated structures – the soft and hard palates, teeth and gums, tongue, palatine tonsils, and salivary glands. In the adult, 32 permanent teeth are arranged in two arcades of 16 teeth each. The tongue is a muscular organ attached to the floor of the mouth. On each side, the tongue is joined to the palate by the palatoglossal arches, and immediately behind these arches are the palatine tonsils. The principal salivary glands are the parotid, submandibular, and sublingual glands, which drain into the mouth through separate ducts. Lining the abdominal cavity, and also extending out into the cavity to cover the organs within, is the thin lubricating membrane of the peritoneum. Folds of the peritoneum attach the organs to the back of the abdominal cavity. Other folds of the peritoneum – the mesenteries and omenta – provide a route for the passage of nerves, blood vessels, and lymphatics.

Oral Cavity – sagittal view

1. _____
2. _____
3. _____
4. _____
5. _____
6. _____
7. _____

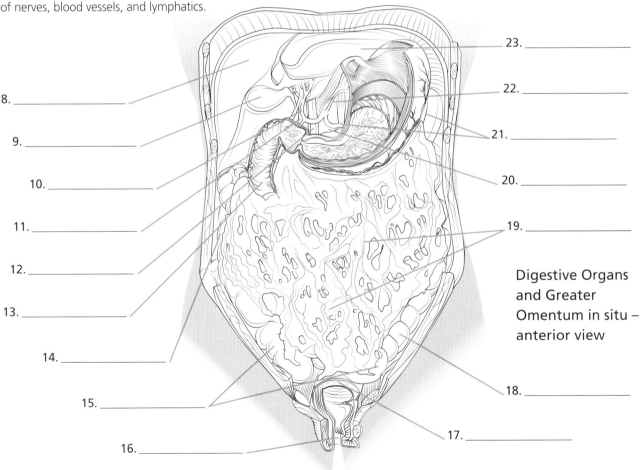

Digestive Organs and Greater Omentum in situ – anterior view

8. _____
9. _____
10. _____
11. _____
12. _____
13. _____
14. _____
15. _____
16. _____
17. _____
18. _____
19. _____
20. _____
21. _____
22. _____
23. _____

Answers

1. Soft palate, 2. Hard palate, 3. Incisors, 4. Tongue, 5. Laryngopharynx, 6. Oesophagus, 7. Trachea, 8. Liver (right lobe, reflected), 9. Gallbladder, 10. Hepatic artery, 11. Portal vein, 12. Inferior vena cava, 13. Duodenum, 14. Ascending colon, 15. Small intestine, 16. Anus, 17. Rectum, 18. Sigmoid colon, 19. Greater omentum, 20. Abdominal aorta, 21. Splenic artery, 22. Left gastric artery, 23. Liver (left lobe, reflected)

Oral Cavity

The bulk of the tongue is made of muscle. The dorsum of the tongue is studded with papillae, of which there are three types in humans: filiform, fungiform, and vallate. The pharyngeal part of the tongue contains the lingual tonsil. Teeth are calcified bone-like structures in both jaws. The crown of a tooth is covered with enamel. Under the enamel is dentin, which makes up the main part of the tooth. The dentin below the gum line is covered with cementum, a hard bony substance covering the roots of the teeth. Dentin is a sensitive tissue, with millions of tubules running into the central pulp or nerve. The cementum is surrounded by the periodontal ligament, which holds the tooth in the jaw.

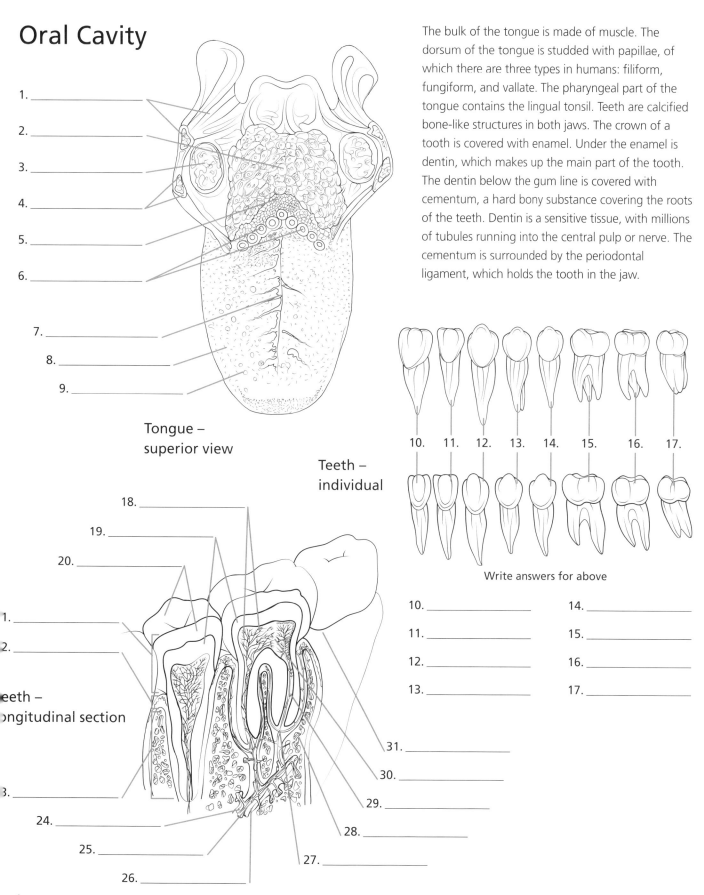

1. _____
2. _____
3. _____
4. _____
5. _____
6. _____
7. _____
8. _____
9. _____

Tongue – superior view

Teeth – individual

10. 11. 12. 13. 14. 15. 16. 17.

Write answers for above

10. _____ 14. _____
11. _____ 15. _____
12. _____ 16. _____
13. _____ 17. _____

18. _____
19. _____
20. _____
1. _____
2. _____

Teeth – longitudinal section

3. _____
24. _____
25. _____
26. _____
27. _____
28. _____
29. _____
30. _____
31. _____

Answers

1. Palatopharyngeal arch and muscle, 2. Lingual tonsil, 3. Palatine tonsil, 4. Palatoglossal arch and muscle, 5. Terminal sulcus, 6. Vallate papillae, 7. Median sulcus, 8. Filiform papilla, 9. Fungiform papilla, 10. Central incisor, 11. Lateral incisor, 12. Canine, 13. First premolar, 14. Second premolar, 15. Third molar, 16. Second molar, 17. First molar, 18. Capillary plexus, 19. Dentin, 20. Enamel, 21. Crown of tooth, 22. Neck of tooth, 23. Root of tooth, 24. Alveolar vein, 25. Alveolar artery, 26. Alveolar nerve, 27. Apical foramen, 28. Alveolar process, 29. Root canal, 30. Pulp cavity, 31. Gingiva

Oral Cavity

Oral Cavity and
Salivary Glands –
anterior view

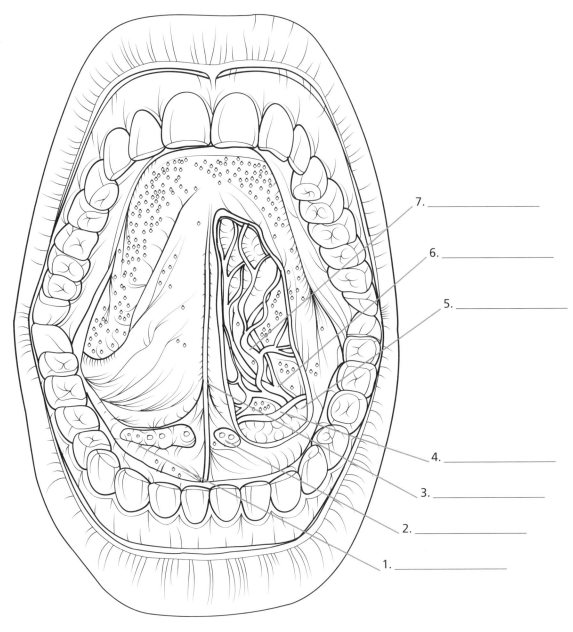

7. _____

6. _____

5. _____

4. _____

3. _____

2. _____

1. _____

The underside of the tongue is soft and is kept moist by salivary gland secretions. The salivary glands are located around the oral cavity and are divided into two groups. The major salivary glands consist of three pairs of glands: the parotid, submandibular, and sublingual glands. The minor buccal salivary glands are microscopic and are scattered around the mouth, palate, and throat. The parotid gland is located in front of each ear. The submandibular gland is located below the jaw (mandible) on each side of the neck, about 2.5 centimetres in front of the angle of the jaw. The sublingual glands are small and lie within ridges on the floor of the mouth, beneath the tongue. The frenulum forms a midline ridge on the lower surface of the tongue. Beneath this ridge lie paired deep arteries and veins of the tongue.

Answers

1. Sublingual folds (with openings of sublingual ducts), 2. Sublingual caruncle (with opening of submandibular duct), 3. Frenulum, 4. Submandibular duct, 5. Sublingual gland, 6. Lingual nerve, 7. Deep lingual vein

Salivary Glands – lateral view

1. _____

2. _____

3. _____

4. _____

5. _____

6. _____

7. _____

8. _____

9. _____

10. _____

Sialolithiasis

The salivary glands secrete saliva into the oral cavity through a series of ducts. Sialolithiasis is a condition where a calcified body or stone (sialolith) forms within the duct of a salivary gland, often the duct of the submandibular gland. The sialolith blocks the flow of salivary fluid, leading to pain and swelling in the affected gland. This pain may worsen when the sight, thought, or smell of food stimulates salivary gland secretion. The condition is treated by removal of the stone, but excision of the gland may be necessary if there is a recurrence.

Answers

1. Accessory parotid gland, 2. Parotid duct, 3. Tongue, 4. Frenulum, 5. Sublingual gland, 6. Submandibular gland, 7. Facial vein, 8. Internal jugular vein, 9. Masseter muscle, 10. Parotid gland

Oral Cavity

1. _____
2. _____
3. _____
4. _____
5. _____
6. _____
7. _____
8. _____

Parotid Gland (cellular level)

The salivary glands secrete saliva into the mouth. This fluid is needed to moisten food to ease swallowing and to begin food breakdown. The three pairs of salivary glands are the parotid, sublingual, and submandibular glands. Each pair has a unique cellular organisation and produces saliva with slightly different properties. The thin saliva produced by the parotid glands contains enzymes specially designed to break down starch. Each submandibular gland comprises a mixture of enzyme-producing serous cells and mucous-producing cells. Its saliva is predominantly water. This gland produces thicker, watery mucous, particularly in response to milk or cream, which helps to lubricate the mouth.

Answers

1. Acinus, 2. Serous cell, 3. Striated duct, 4. Vein, 5. Interlobular duct, 6. Septum of connective tissue, 7. Artery, 8. Intercalated ducts

Submandibular Gland
(cellular level)

1. _____

2. _____

6. _____

3. _____

4. _____

5. _____

Sublingual Gland
(cellular level)

7. _____

8. _____

9. _____

10. _____

11. _____

12. _____

Answers

Liver and Gallbladder

The liver is the heaviest internal organ in the body, and it is found under the cover and protection of the lower ribs, on the right side of the abdomen. The liver has an upper (diaphragmatic) surface and a lower (visceral) surface; the two surfaces are separated at the front by a sharp inferior border. The liver is attached to the diaphragm by the falciform, triangular, and coronary ligaments. The liver is also joined to the stomach and duodenum by the gastrohepatic and hepatoduodenal ligaments, respectively. The visceral surface of the liver is in contact with the gallbladder, the right kidney, part of the duodenum, the oesophagus, the stomach, and the hepatic flexure of the colon. The porta hepatis – the point where vessels and ducts enter and exit the liver – lies on the visceral surface. Microscopically, the liver contains sheets of cells (hepatocytes) arranged in hexagonal prism-shaped lobules. The space between the sheets of hepatocytes is filled with small blood vessels called liver sinusoids. Branches of both the portal vein and hepatic artery feed into these sinusoids. A system of bile ductules runs between the hepatocytes. These ductules carry bile produced by the hepatocytes. The ductules eventually join together to form intrahepatic bile ducts, which in turn join together to form the bile duct. At the corners of each hexagonal liver lobule lie a branch of the portal vein, hepatic artery, and bile duct, while the centre of each lobule is occupied by a central vein.

6. _____

5. _____

Liver – anterior view

4. _____

3. _____

2. _____

1. _____

16. _____

17. _____

15. _____

7. _____

8. _____

9. _____

10. _____

11. _____

14. _____

Liver – posterior view

12. _____

13. _____

Answers

Liver Lobule – cellular level

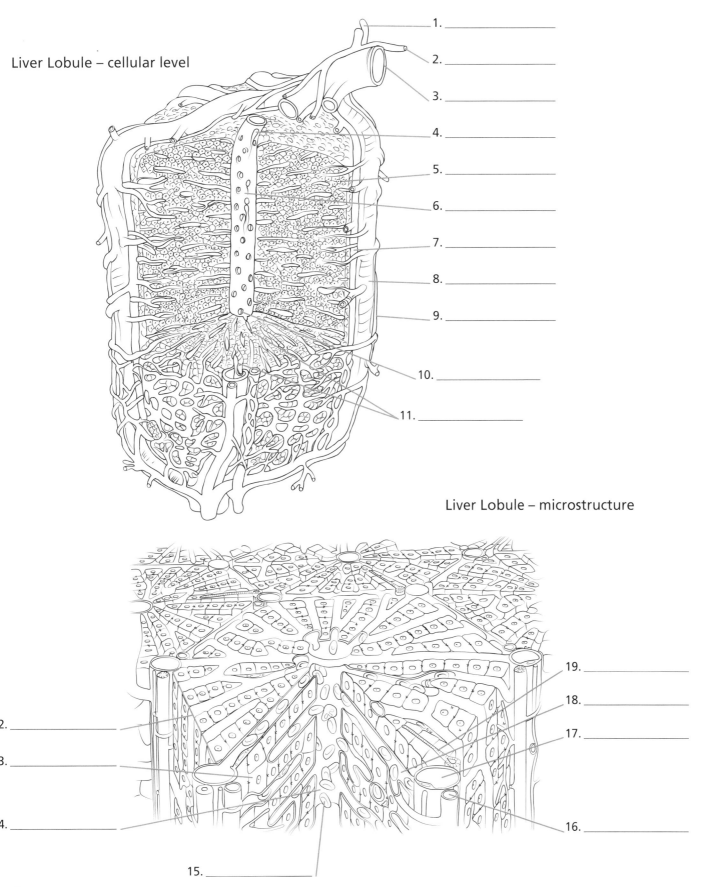

1. _____
2. _____
3. _____
4. _____
5. _____
6. _____
7. _____
8. _____
9. _____
10. _____
11. _____

Liver Lobule – microstructure

19. _____
18. _____
17. _____
16. _____

2. _____
3. _____
4. _____
15. _____

Answers

1. Bile duct, 2. Artery, 3. Collecting vein, 4. Sublobular (intercalated) vein, 5. Hepatocyte, 6. Central vein, 7. Interlobular bile duct, 8. Branch of portal vein, 9. Branch of hepatic artery, 10. Opening of a liver sinusoid, 11. Liver sinusoids, 12. Hepatocyte plate, 13. Hepatocyte, 14. Central vein, 15. Red blood cell, 16. Hepatic artery branch, 17. Portal vein branch, 18. Sinusoid, 19. Bile canaliculus

Liver and Gallbladder

The gallbladder is a sac-shaped organ attached to the lower surface of the liver and lies on the right side of the abdomen. The gallbladder stores bile and is part of the biliary tree. The duct of the gallbladder is called the cystic duct. The hepatic ducts carry bile from the liver either to the gallbladder for storage or to the duodenum for usage. The left and right hepatic ducts join to form the common bile duct, which transports bile to the duodenum. The cystic duct transports bile from the gallbladder to the common bile duct. The portal system is the network of veins connecting the major components of the digestive tract to the liver. The primary veins in this network are the superior mesenteric, splenic, and inferior mesenteric veins, which join to form the portal vein. Also draining into the portal vein are the left gastric vein and the cystic veins.

Gallbladder – anterior view

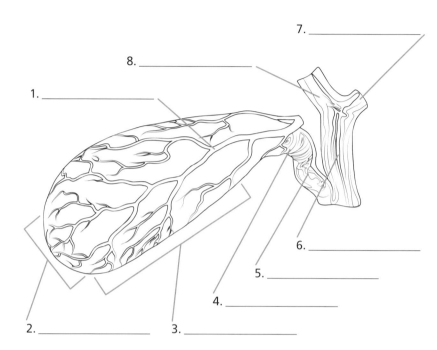

7. _____

8. _____

1. _____

6. _____

5. _____

4. _____

2. _____

3. _____

Bile Ducts – anterior view

9. _____

10. _____

11. _____

1. _____

2. _____

3. _____

4. _____

5. _____

6. _____

7. _____

8. _____

9. _____

10. _____

11. _____

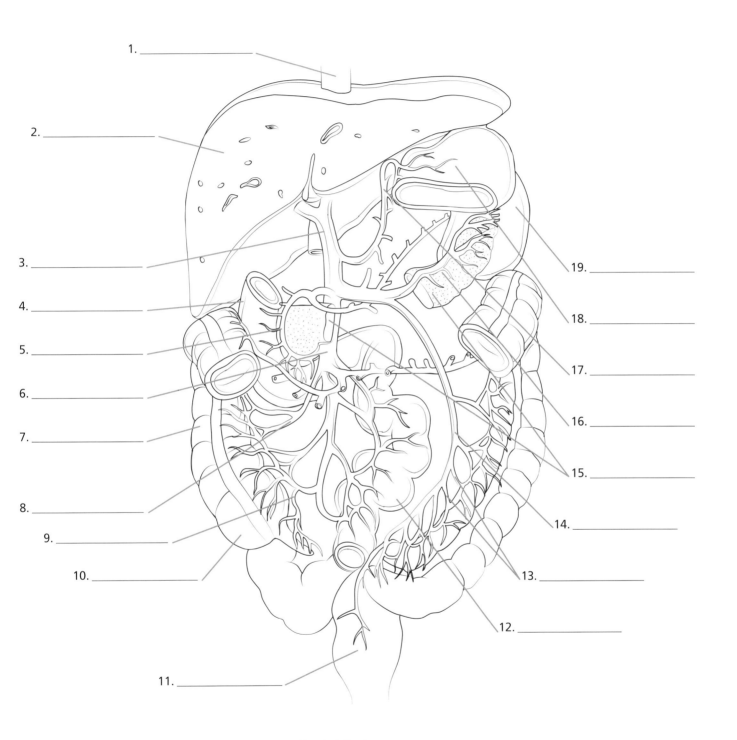

19. _____

18. _____

17. _____

16. _____

15. _____

14. _____

13. _____

12. _____

Portal System
(digestive function) –
anterior view

Answers

Pancreas, Stomach, and Intestines

1. _____
2. _____
3. _____
4. _____
5. _____
6. _____
7. _____

Pancreas (digestive function) – anterior view

The pancreas is an elongated gland lying behind the stomach and in front of the aorta and inferior vena cava. Extending from the large head of the pancreas are the neck, body, and tail of the pancreas. Pancreatic secretions are collected by the main pancreatic duct and accessory pancreatic duct. The parts of the stomach are the cardia (located at the gastro-oesophageal junction), the fundus, the body, and the pylorus. The muscles of the stomach churn food and move food from the body of the stomach to the pylorus. The pyloric canal is encircled by the pyloric sphincter, a ring of smooth muscle that controls the passage of stomach juices and food.

Carcinoma of the pancreas

Cancer may arise in the exocrine glandular tissue of the pancreas, and this type of cancer has one of the worst survival rates of any common cancer in the Western world. Some patients present with nausea, vomiting, and weakness, but often the first sign is severe abdominal pain from the tumour invading nearby nerves. If the cancer is in the head of the pancreas, the bile duct may be obstructed, causing back-up of bile to the liver and leading to jaundice (yellow skin), loss of appetite, dark urine, and light-coloured stools.

Answers

1. Neck (of pancreas), 2. Head (of pancreas), 3. Accessory pancreatic duct, 4. Main pancreatic duct, 5. Uncinate process, 6. Tail (of pancreas), 7. Body (of pancreas)

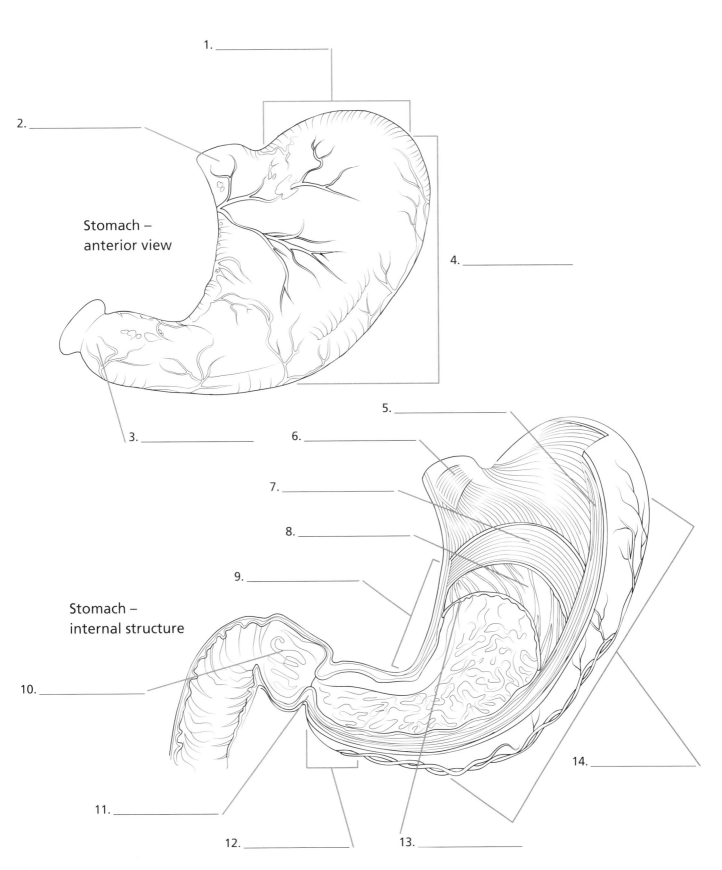

1. _____

2. _____

Stomach –
anterior view

4. _____

3. _____

5. _____

6. _____

7. _____

8. _____

9. _____

Stomach –
internal structure

10. _____

14. _____

11. _____

12. _____

13. _____

Answers

1. Fundus (of stomach), 2. Cardia, 3. Pyloric region, 4. Body (of stomach), 5. Longitudinal muscle layer, 6. Cardiac muscle, 7. Circular muscle, 8. Submucosal neurovascular layer, 9. Lesser curvature, 10. Duodenum (first part), 11. Pyloric sphincter, 12. Pylorus (of stomach), 13. Mucosa and submucosa, 14. Greater curvature

Pancreas, Stomach, and Intestines

The stomach and small and large intestines are the principal organs involved in the breakdown and processing of food. The intestines occupy the lower two-thirds of the abdominal cavity and consist of two parts: the small intestine (duodenum, jejunum, and ileum) and the large intestine (colon and rectum). The small intestine leads on from the stomach, and the large intestine leads on from the small intestine. The large intestine is composed of an initial part called the caecum, with the vermiform appendix attached, and the ascending colon, transverse colon, descending colon, sigmoid colon, and rectum. The small and large intestines are covered by smooth muscle, with an inner circular layer that is thicker than the outer longitudinal layer. The lining of the intestines has many small transverse folds (plicae) and tiny projections (villi). The number of villi diminishes from the ileum to the rectum.

Jejunum – cross-sectional view

11. _____

10. _____

9. _____

8. _____

1. _____

2. _____

3. _____

4. _____

5. _____

6. _____

7. _____

12. _____

13. _____

14. _____

15. _____

16. _____

17. _____

18. _____

24. _____

23. _____

22. _____

21. _____

20. _____

19. _____

Stomach and Intestines – anterior view

Answers

1. Serosa (mesothelium), 2. Serosa (connective tissue), 3. Plica circularis, 4. Submucosa, 5. Muscularis externa (outer longitudinal fibres), 6. Mucosa, 7. Muscularis mucosae, 8. Nerves of the mesenteric plexus, 9. Muscularis externa (inner circular layer), 10. Villi, 11. Villi, 12. Duodenum, 13. Mesentery, 14. Ascending colon, 15. Caecum, 16. Appendix, 17. Rectum, 18. Anus, 19. Ileum, 20. Sigmoid colon, 21. Jejunum, 22. Pylorus (of stomach), 23. Ascending colon, 24. Stomach

Intestinal Villus – cross-sectional view

1. _____

2. _____

3. _____

9. _____

8. _____

7. _____

6. _____

5. _____

4. _____

The plicae and villi on the lining of the duodenum and jejunum greatly increase the surface area available for the absorption of nutrients. The rectum is the second-to-last part of the digestive tract. Its upper part has a series of folds in its walls called rectal valves. At the lower end of the rectum are longitudinally running folds called anal (or rectal) columns. The anus is a short tube leading from the rectum through the anal sphincter to the anal orifice. The anus is closed by an involuntary and a voluntary anal sphincter – the internal and external anal sphincter, respectively.

Anus – coronal view

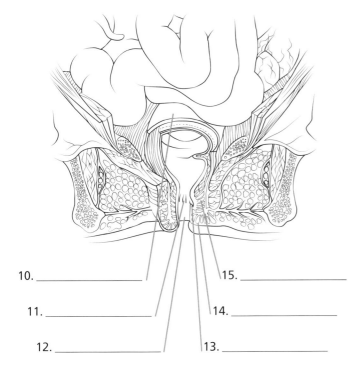

10. _____

11. _____

12. _____

15. _____

14. _____

13. _____

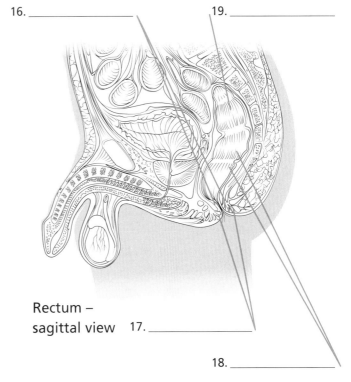

16. _____

19. _____

17. _____

18. _____

Rectum – sagittal view

Answers

1. Villus, 2. Circular muscular layer, 3. Longitudinal muscular layer, 4. Mucosa of small intestine, 5. Lamina propria, 6. Basal lamina, 7. Intestinal epithelium, 8. Lymphatic lacteal, 9. Lymphocytes, 10. Rectum, 11. Anal column, 12. Anus, 13. Anal valve, 14. External anal sphincter, 15. Internal anal sphincter, 16. Internal anal sphincter, 17. External anal sphincter, 18. Rectum, 19. Sigmoid colon

Urinary System

Male Urinary System –
anterior view

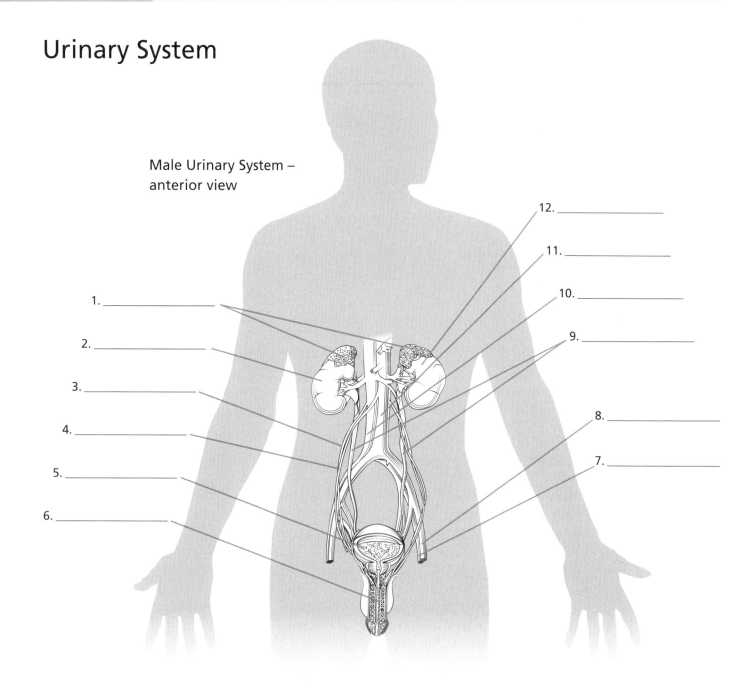

1. _____

2. _____

3. _____

4. _____

5. _____

6. _____

12. _____

11. _____

10. _____

9. _____

8. _____

7. _____

The urinary system excretes the waste products of metabolism and maintains the balance of water and electrolytes in the blood. The urinary system consists of the kidneys, the ureters, the bladder, and the urethra. Waste products are filtered out of the blood by the kidneys and excreted in the urine, which is carried into the bladder by the ureters. The rear surface of the bladder is in front of the rectum and receives the ureters. The openings of the two ureters and the urethra form the three corners of the triangular trigone. The male urethra emerges from the neck of the bladder and passes through the prostate gland and the membrane formed by the muscle layers of the floor of the pelvis before reaching the penis. The male urethra is the passage for both urine and sperm.

Answers

Female Urinary System – anterior view

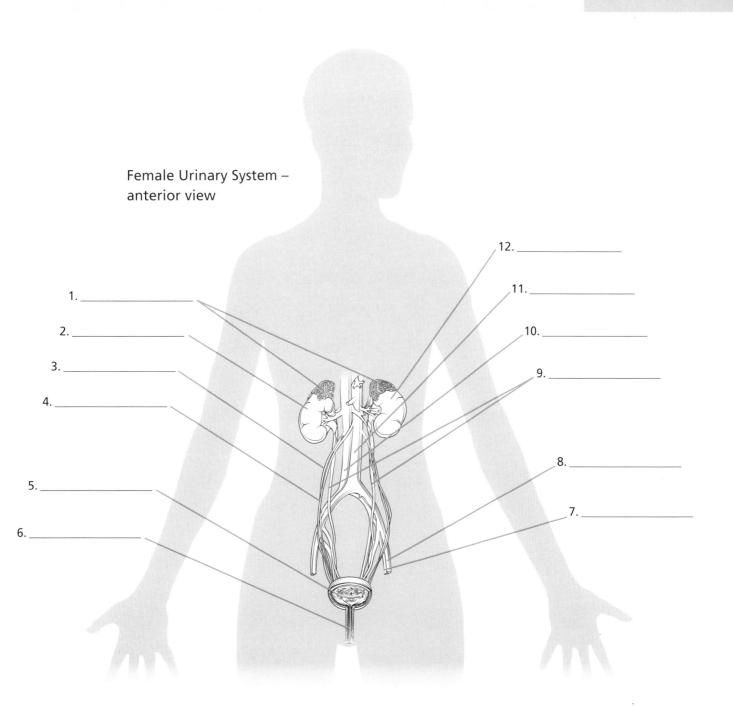

1. _____
2. _____
3. _____
4. _____
5. _____
6. _____

7. _____
8. _____
9. _____
10. _____
11. _____
12. _____

The kidneys, the ureters, the bladder, and the urethra make up the urinary system, and the structure and organisation of the system is similar in both sexes from the kidney down to the bladder. The vagina lies between the rectum and the rear surface of the bladder, with the uterus lying on top of the bladder. The urethra passes directly through the pelvic floor. Because the female urethra is not involved in the reproductive system, it is very short and opens in front of the entrance of the vagina.

Answers

Kidneys and Urinary Tract

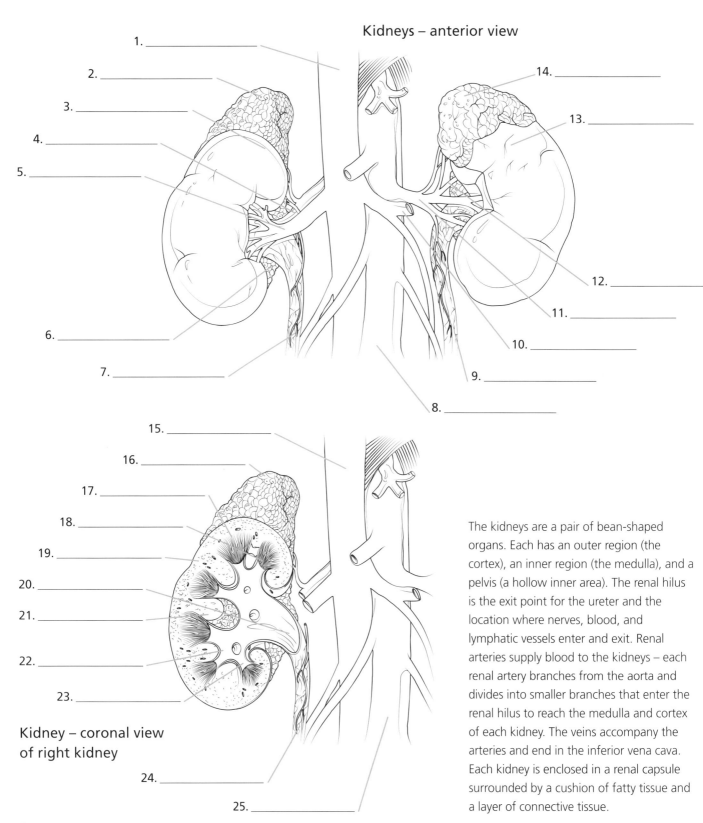

Kidneys – anterior view

1. _____
2. _____
3. _____
4. _____
5. _____
6. _____
7. _____
8. _____
9. _____
10. _____
11. _____
12. _____
13. _____
14. _____

15. _____
16. _____
17. _____
18. _____
19. _____
20. _____
21. _____
22. _____
23. _____
24. _____
25. _____

Kidney – coronal view
of right kidney

The kidneys are a pair of bean-shaped organs. Each has an outer region (the cortex), an inner region (the medulla), and a pelvis (a hollow inner area). The renal hilus is the exit point for the ureter and the location where nerves, blood, and lymphatic vessels enter and exit. Renal arteries supply blood to the kidneys – each renal artery branches from the aorta and divides into smaller branches that enter the renal hilus to reach the medulla and cortex of each kidney. The veins accompany the arteries and end in the inferior vena cava. Each kidney is enclosed in a renal capsule surrounded by a cushion of fatty tissue and a layer of connective tissue.

Answers

1. Inferior vena cava, 2. Right adrenal gland, 3. Right adrenal gland, 4. Right kidney, 5. Right renal artery, 6. Perirenal fat, 7. Right ureter, 8. Abdominal aorta, 9. Left ureter, 10. Left renal vein, 11. Left renal artery, 12. Segmental artery, 13. Left kidney, 14. Left adrenal gland, 15. Inferior vena cava, 16. Right adrenal gland, 17. Renal pyramid (medulla), 18. Tip of renal papilla, 19. Cortex, 20. Renal pelvis, 21. Renal column, 22. Major calyx, 23. Minor calyx, 24. Right ureter, 25. Abdominal aorta

Urinary Tract – anterior view

1. _____
2. _____
3. _____
4. _____
5. _____
6. _____
7. _____
8. _____

17. _____
16. _____

9. _____
10. _____
11. _____
12. _____
13. _____

15. _____
14. _____

Nephron

The kidneys filter the blood, removing metabolic waste products. The right kidney lies behind the duodenum; the left lies behind the pancreas and stomach. The adrenal glands cap the upper tip of each kidney. The renal pelvis of the kidney continues into the ureter, which carries urine from the kidney to the bladder. The bladder expels urine from the body via the urethra once the bladder is full. Nephrons are tiny urine-producing units found in the kidney. There are millions of nephrons located in both kidneys. Each nephron is composed of a capillary tuft (the glomerulus) and a tubule that extends from the glomerulus. The blood is filtered, giving rise to fluid (urine) that flows through the tubule. The tubule has a proximal part, the loop of Henle, and a distal part.

Answers

1. Adrenal glands, 2. Right kidney, 3. Left kidney, 4. Inferior vena cava, 5. Abdominal aorta, 6. Right ureter, 7. Left ureter, 8. Urinary bladder, 9. Afferent arteriole, 10. Glomerular capillaries, 11. Bowman's capsule around a glomerulus, 12. Glomerulus, 13. Artery, 14. Loop of Henle, 15. Capillary network, 16. Proximal convoluted tubule, 17. Efferent arteriole

Urinary Tract and Bladder

Urine flows from the kidneys through the ureters to the bladder. The ureters are two muscular tubes, the walls of which contain smooth muscles that contract and propel urine in waves into the bladder, a muscular sac that resembles an inverted pyramid. The rear surface of the bladder receives the ureters. The urethra emerges from the neck of the bladder, which is located at the bottom of the bladder. The openings of the two ureters and the urethra form the three corners of the triangular trigone. Two muscles – internal and external urethral sphincter muscles – work in unison to control elimination of urine. The internal urethral sphincter muscle is controlled by the autonomic nervous system, alerting the brain when the bladder is full. The external urethral sphincter is under voluntary control, and only when this muscle is relaxed does the internal sphincter also relax, allowing the elimination of urine. The urethra carries urine from the bladder to the outside of the body. The male urethra is usually 20 centimetres long, passes from the bladder through the prostate gland, where it is joined by the sperm ducts, and opens at the tip of the penis. Essentially similar in structure to the male urinary system, the female urinary system features a shorter urethra than that of the male. Urine passes along the ureters to the bladder and then is expelled from the body via the urethra, which opens out in front of the entrance to the vagina.

Urinary Tract (male) – sagittal view

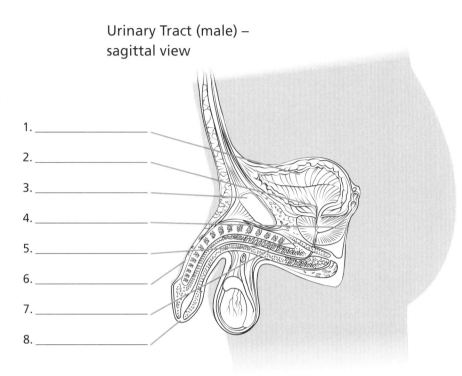

1. _____
2. _____
3. _____
4. _____
5. _____
6. _____
7. _____
8. _____

Urinary Tract (female) – sagittal view

9. _____
10. _____
11. _____
12. _____
13. _____
14. _____
15. _____

Bladder (male) –
anterior view

Bladder (male) –
posterior view

Bladder (female) –
anterior view

1. _____
2. _____
3. _____
4. _____
5. _____
6. _____
7. _____
8. _____
9. _____
10. _____
11. _____
12. _____
13. _____
14. _____
15. _____
16. _____
17. _____
18. _____
19. _____
20. _____
21. _____
22. _____
23. _____
24. _____
25. _____
28. _____
29. _____
30. _____
31. _____
32. _____
33. _____
34. _____
35. _____
36. _____
37. _____
38. _____
39. _____
40. _____
41. _____
42. _____
43. _____
44. _____
45. _____
46. _____
47. _____
48. _____
49. _____
50. _____
51. _____
52. _____

Answers

1. Right inferior vena cava. 2. Right testicular vein. 3. Right testicular artery. 4. Right internal iliac artery. 5. Right ureter. 6. Bladder. 7. Opening (meatus) of right ureter. 8. Prostate gland. 9. Penis. 10. Scrotum. 11. Urethral meatus (opening). 12. Spongy urethra. 13. Bulb of penis. 14. Bulbourethral (Cowper's) gland. 15. Urethra. 16. Neck of bladder. 17. Left external iliac artery. 18. Left external iliac vein. 19. Opening (meatus) of left ureter. 20. Left internal iliac vein. 21. Left internal iliac artery. 22. Left common iliac vein. 23. Left common iliac artery. 24. Left ureter. 25. Peritoneum. 26. Left ureter. 27. Membranous urethra. 28. Bulbourethral (Cowper's) glands. 29. Prostatic urethra. 30. Prostate gland. 31. Ejaculatory duct. 32. Seminal vesicle. 33. Ampulla of ductus deferens. 34. Ductus deferens. 35. Right ureter. 36. Detrusor muscle of bladder. 37. Right inferior vena cava. 38. Right ovarian vein. 39. Right ovarian artery. 40. Right ureter. 41. Right internal iliac artery. 42. Opening (meatus) of right ureter. 43. Urethra. 44. Trigone. 45. Opening (meatus) of left ureter. 46. Left internal iliac vein. 47. Left external iliac artery. 48. Left external iliac vein. 49. Left common iliac vein. 50. Left common iliac artery. 51. Left ureter. 52. Abdominal aorta

Endocrine System

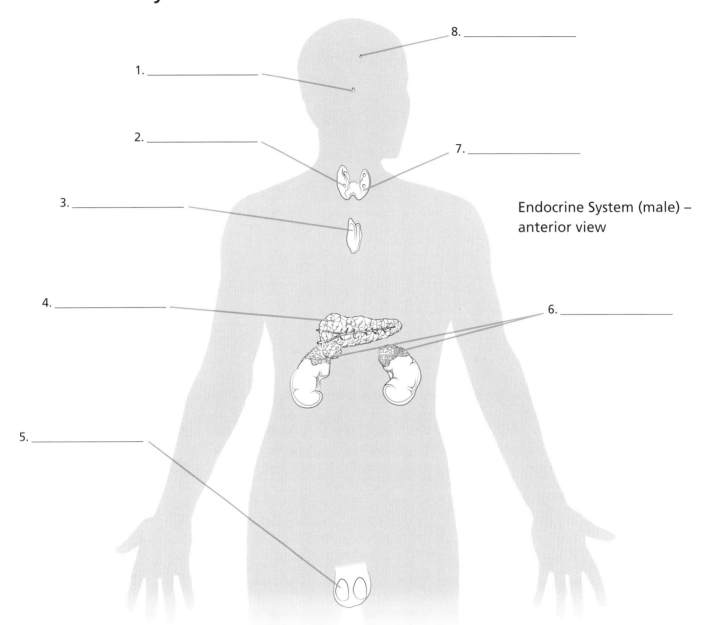

1. _____

2. _____

3. _____

4. _____

5. _____

6. _____

7. _____

8. _____

Endocrine System (male) –
anterior view

The endocrine system, involved in coordinating the activities of tissues throughout the body, acts by means of hormones. Hormones are released from endocrine cells at specific times and in precise amounts to act on target organs, at some distance from their site of release. Endocrine organs (often called endocrine glands) secrete only into the bloodstream. Hormones usually act by binding with special receptor sites on or inside target cells. The organs involved in the male endocrine systems are the pituitary, pineal, thymus, thyroid, parathyroids, adrenals, pancreatic islets, and testes. The testes produce hormones that control sexual function and secondary sexual characteristics.

Answers

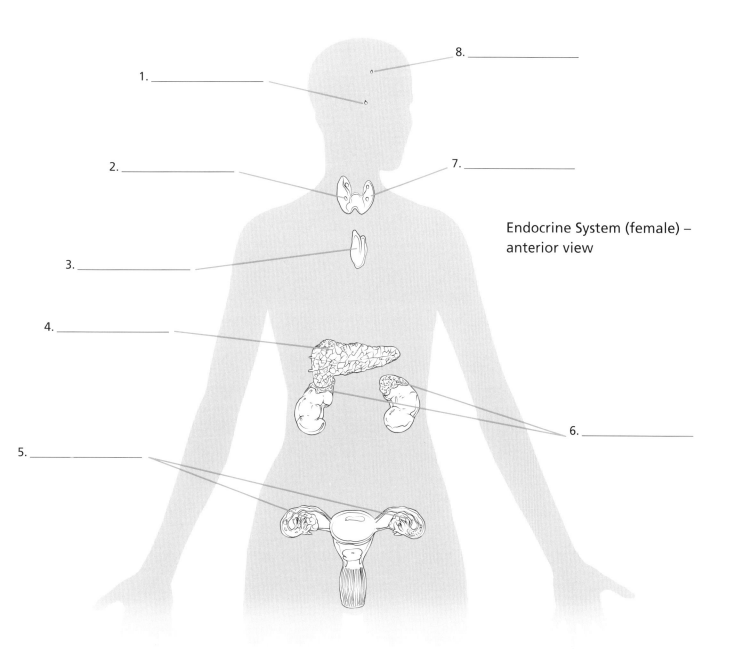

1. _____

2. _____

3. _____

4. _____

5. _____

6. _____

7. _____

8. _____

Endocrine System (female) – anterior view

The endocrine and nervous systems share control of body functions: the nervous system usually controls activities occurring rapidly or in the short term, while the endocrine system controls slow or long-term changes. Endocrine hormones affect the nervous system, and many endocrine organs are stimulated or inhibited by nerve cells. The hypothalamus of the brain has an intimate connection with the chief organ of the endocrine system, the pituitary. The endocrine system acts under the control of the pituitary gland. The organs involved in the female endocrine system include the pituitary, pineal, thymus, thyroid, parathyroids, adrenals, pancreatic islets, ovaries, and placenta (during pregnancy). The ovaries produce hormones that control sexual function and secondary sexual characteristics.

Answers

1. Pituitary gland, 2. Parathyroid, 3. Thymus, 4. Pancreas, 5. Ovaries, 6. Adrenal glands, 7. Thyroid gland, 8. Pineal gland

Endocrine Glands

The pituitary gland (hypophysis) is a very small organ lying immediately below the hypothalamus of the brain. The pituitary gland is divided into anterior and posterior lobes (the adenohypophysis and neurohypophysis, respectively). The anterior lobe contains many different types of cells, which produce growth hormone, prolactin, follicle-stimulating hormone, luteinising hormone, thyroid-stimulating hormone, adrenocorticotrophic hormone, and melanocyte-stimulating hormone. The posterior lobe contains oxytocin and antidiuretic hormones, produced in the hypothalamus and transported to the pituitary within nerve fibres. The pineal gland (body) is also small and is located inside the skull cavity, surrounded by the brain. The pineal gland produces melatonin, whose concentration varies in tune with the 24-hour cycle of the day (circadian rhythm) – melatonin production is highest during a person's normal sleeping hours and drops off as the body begins to wake. The pineal gland probably has an effect on the ovaries and testes and may influence mood.

1. _____

2. _____

3. _____

4. _____

Pineal Gland

5. _____

6. _____

7. _____

8. _____

14. _____

13. _____

12. _____

11. _____

9. _____   10. _____

Pituitary Gland

Answers

1. Cerebrum, 2. Pineal gland, 3. Brainstem, 4. Cerebellum, 5. Neurosecretory cell, 6. Optic chiasm, 7. Infundibulum, 8. Hypophyseal artery, 9. Anterior pituitary (adenohypophysis), 10. Posterior pituitary (neurohypophysis), 11. Hypophyseal portal system, 12. Axon, 13. Mammillary body, 14. Hypothalamus

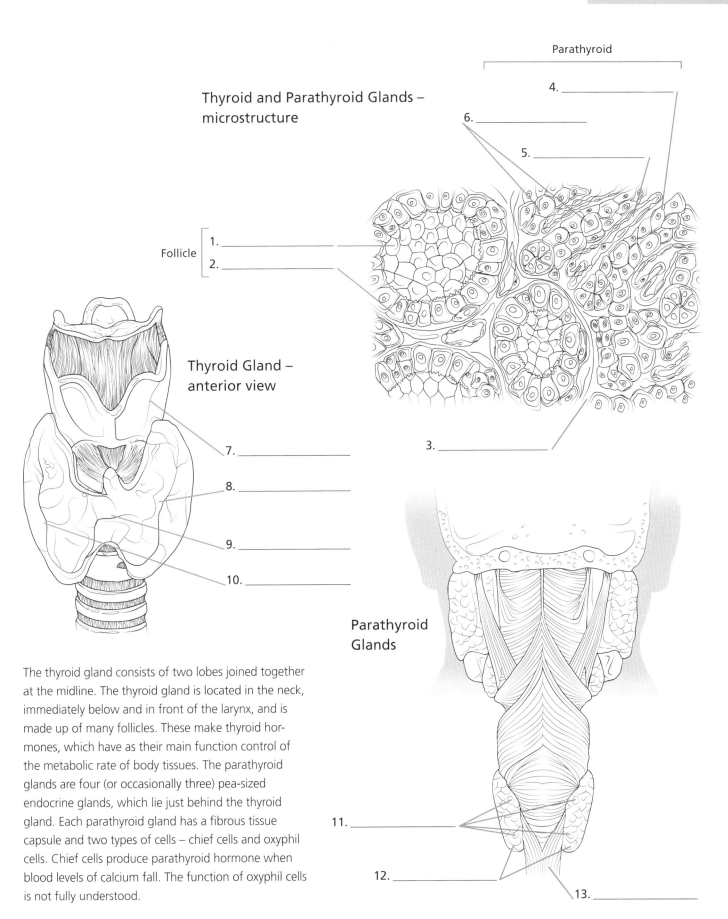

Thyroid and Parathyroid Glands –
microstructure

Parathyroid

4. _____

6. _____

5. _____

Follicle
1. _____
2. _____

3. _____

Thyroid Gland –
anterior view

7. _____

8. _____

9. _____

10. _____

Parathyroid
Glands

11. _____

12. _____

13. _____

The thyroid gland consists of two lobes joined together at the midline. The thyroid gland is located in the neck, immediately below and in front of the larynx, and is made up of many follicles. These make thyroid hormones, which have as their main function control of the metabolic rate of body tissues. The parathyroid glands are four (or occasionally three) pea-sized endocrine glands, which lie just behind the thyroid gland. Each parathyroid gland has a fibrous tissue capsule and two types of cells – chief cells and oxyphil cells. Chief cells produce parathyroid hormone when blood levels of calcium fall. The function of oxyphil cells is not fully understood.

Answers

1. Lumen filled with colloid, 2. Thyroid epithelium, 3. Capsule of parathyroid, 4. Chief cell, 5. Capillary, 6. Oxyphil cells, 7. Thyroid cartilage (of larynx), 8. Left lobe of thyroid gland, 9. Isthmus of thyroid gland, 10. Right lobe of thyroid gland, 11. Parathyroid glands, 12. Thyroid, 13. Oesophagus

Endocrine Glands

The pancreas is an elongated gland lying behind the stomach. The pancreas plays a role in both the digestive and the endocrine systems. Its endocrine function is hormonal and is involved in regulation of glucose mobilisation and storage (the responsible hormones are glucagon and insulin, respectively). These two hormones are produced in special cell types (alpha and beta cells) within many tiny spherical clumps of pancreatic tissue, known as pancreatic islets or the islets of Langerhans. The islets are surrounded by exocrine tissue.

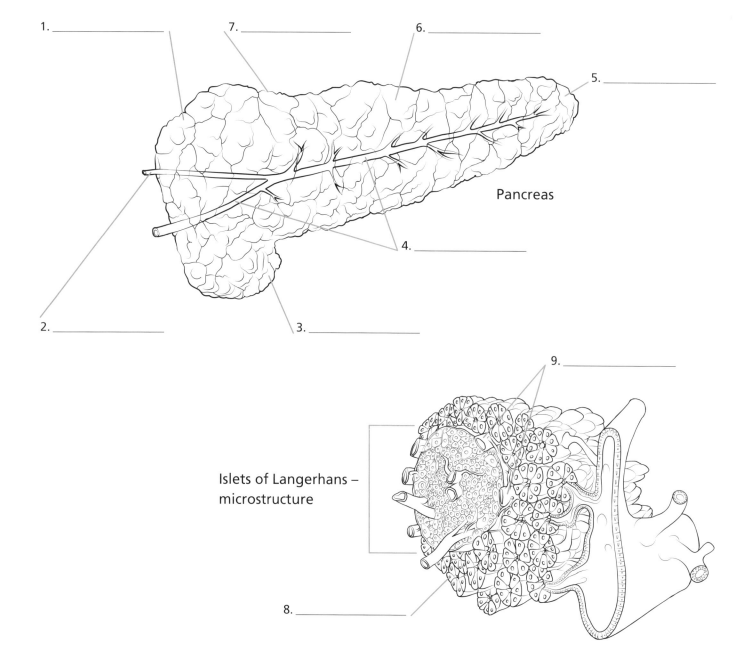

1. _____

7. _____

6. _____

5. _____

2. _____

3. _____

4. _____

Pancreas

9. _____

Islets of Langerhans – microstructure

8. _____

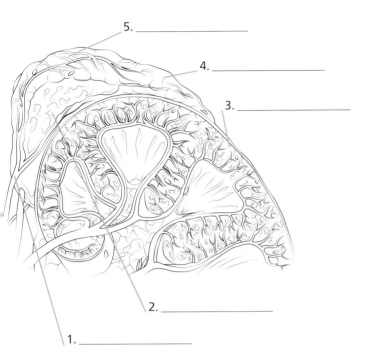

5. _____

4. _____

3. _____

2. _____

1. _____

Adrenal Glands –
coronal section through
left adrenal gland

The two triangular adrenal (or suprarenal) glands lie one on top of each kidney at the back of the abdomen. Each gland has an outer part (the cortex) and a core (the medulla). The adrenal cortex produces three main types of hormones: glucocorticoids, mineralocorticoids, and sex steroids. Glucocorticoids promote the breakdown of protein and the release of fat and sugars into the bloodstream. Mineralocorticoids stimulate the release of sodium in the kidneys. Sex steroids contribute to the development of sexual characteristics. The adrenal medulla contains many modified nerve cells, which produce the hormones epinephrine and norepinephrine (adrenaline and noradrenaline), respectively. These hormones are released in bursts during emergency situations or accompanying intense emotion. They act to increase the strength and rate of heart contraction, raise the blood sugar level, elevate blood pressure, and increase breathing.

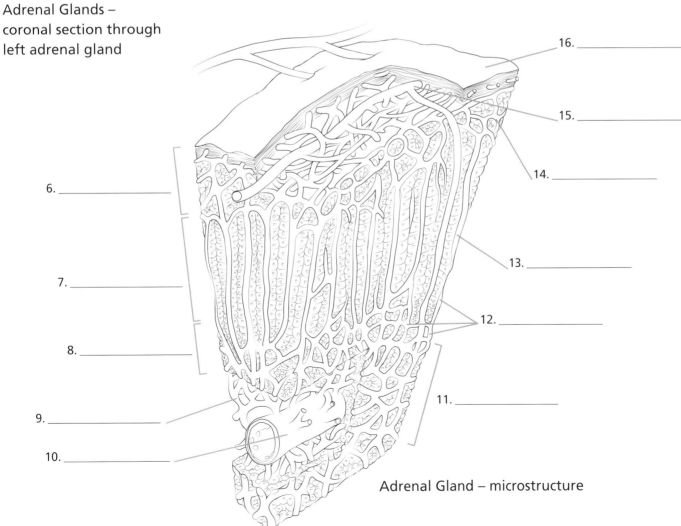

6. _____

7. _____

8. _____

9. _____

10. _____

16. _____

15. _____

14. _____

13. _____

12. _____

11. _____

Adrenal Gland – microstructure

Answers

1. Left suprarenal artery, 2. Left adrenal medulla, 3. Left kidney, 4. Left adrenal gland, 5. Left adrenal cortex, 6. Zona glomerulosa, 7. Zona fasciculata, 8. Zona reticularis, 9. Medullary plexus of veins, 10. Medullary vein, 11. Medulla, 12. Deep plexus of veins, 13. Sinusoidal vessels, 14. Subcapsular plexus of veins, 15. Capsular artery, 16. Capsule

Male and Female Endocrine Glands

Testes – endocrine function

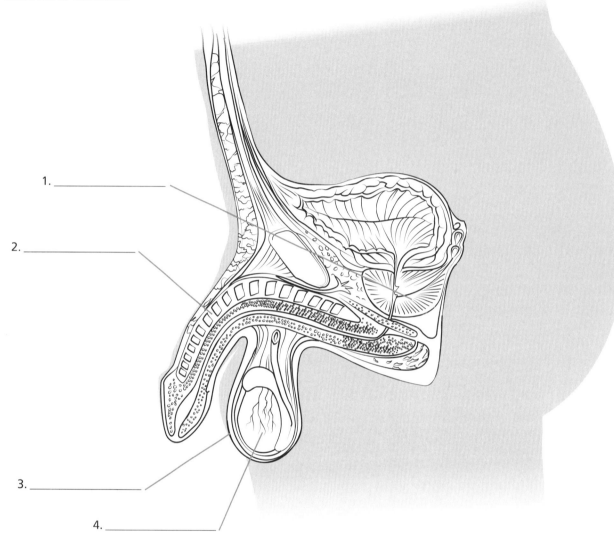

1. _____

2. _____

3. _____

4. _____

The testes are two ovoid organs contained in the scrotum, a sac that lies directly behind and beneath the penis. The testes produce male sex hormones – primarily testosterone. Testosterone is the hormone responsible for the development of secondary sexual characteristics in the male. It stimulates growth of facial and pubic hair, enlargement of the larynx and deepening of the voice, and an increase in muscle tone. Testosterone production is controlled by follicle-stimulating hormone (FSH) and luteinising hormone (LH), both of which are secreted by the anterior lobe of the pituitary gland.

Answers

1. Prostate gland, 2. Penis, 3. Scrotum, 4. Testis

Ovaries – microstructure

9. _____

8. _____

7. _____

1. _____

2. _____

3. _____

4. _____

5. _____

6. _____

The two ovaries are the female gonads in which the ova are formed. They resemble almonds in shape and size, and are situated on either side of the uterus. The ovaries produce the female hormones oestrogen and progesterone. Oestrogen causes growth of the breasts and reproductive organs, among other functions. Progesterone maintains the lining of the uterus in a state suitable to receive a fertilised ovum.

Answers

1. Uterine tube, 2. Mature ovum, 3. Ovum, 4. Ovary, 5. Uterus, 6. Vagina, 7. Corpus luteum, 8. Corpus albicans, 9. Discharging follicle (at ovulation)

Male and Female Endocrine Glands

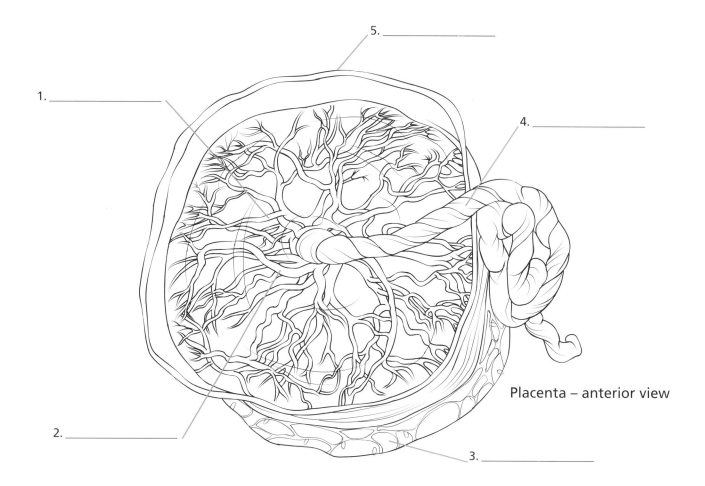

5. _____

1. _____

4. _____

2. _____

3. _____

Placenta – anterior view

An organ of pregnancy, the placenta connects the baby to the mother via the umbilical cord. The placenta also acts as an endocrine organ, producing a hormone to sustain the pregnancy (human chorionic gonadotrophin). HCG is the earliest placental hormone to be produced and is first secreted on day 6 of gestation. HCG maintains the corpus luteum (the ovarian follicle from which the ovum burst) and ensures that it continues to manufacture progesterone and oestrogen until the placenta is able to produce adequate amounts of both, usually by the third month of gestation, when HCG levels decline. The placenta also produces oestrogen, progesterone and relaxin (which relaxes the pelvic ligaments), along with human placental lactogen, which promotes milk production and fetal growth.

Placenta – cross-sectional view

1. _____

2. _____

3. _____

4. _____

5. _____

6. _____

7. _____

8. _____

9. _____

10. _____

Placental insufficiency

The fetus relies on the placenta for all its oxygen and nutrients. Large surface area of the chorionic villi at the fetal side of the placenta is important for effective transfer of nutrients between mother and fetus. Placental insufficiency (also known as uteroplacental vascular insufficiency) is a significant condition where the placenta is unable to supply the necessary nutrients to the fetus. Chronic reduction in oxygen supply to the fetus may cause delay in maturation of the brain, reduced fetal activity, and reduced heart rate. Placental insufficiency may also cause fetal distress, reduced amniotic fluid (oligohydramnios), miscarriage, and stillbirth.

Answers

1. Area filled with maternal blood, 2. Placenta, 3. Endometrium, 4. Maternal blood vessels, 5. Myometrium, 6. Chorionic villi, 7. Syncytial trophoblast, 8. Umbilical arteries, 9. Umbilical vein, 10. Umbilical cord

Male Reproductive System and Organs

Male Reproductive System –
anterior view

1._____

2._____

4._____

3._____

The male reproductive system includes two testes, which produce spermatozoa and male hormones, a system of ducts that convey sperm, glands that contribute secretions to semen, and the external genitalia – the scrotum and penis. Sperm are formed in the testes. During ejaculation, the sperm combine with secretions from the prostate gland and seminal vesicles to form the seminal fluid. The testes are two oval organs contained in the scrotum. Each testis is capped by the epididymis, which becomes the ductus deferens. The ductus deferens and its surrounding vessels and nerves form the contents of the spermatic cord. The ductus deferens then joins the duct of the seminal vesicle to form the ejaculatory duct. The ejaculatory duct opens into the prostatic urethra. The urethra enters and courses through the penis.

Answers

1. Urinary bladder, 2. Prostate gland, 3. Penis, 4. Scrotum

Male Reproductive System –
sagittal view

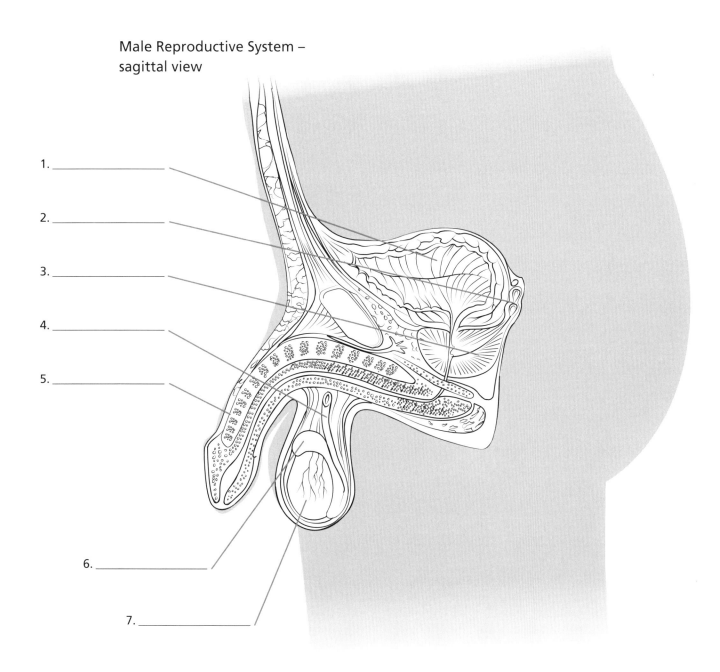

1. _____

2. _____

3. _____

4. _____

5. _____

6. _____

7. _____

Answers

Male Reproductive System and Organs

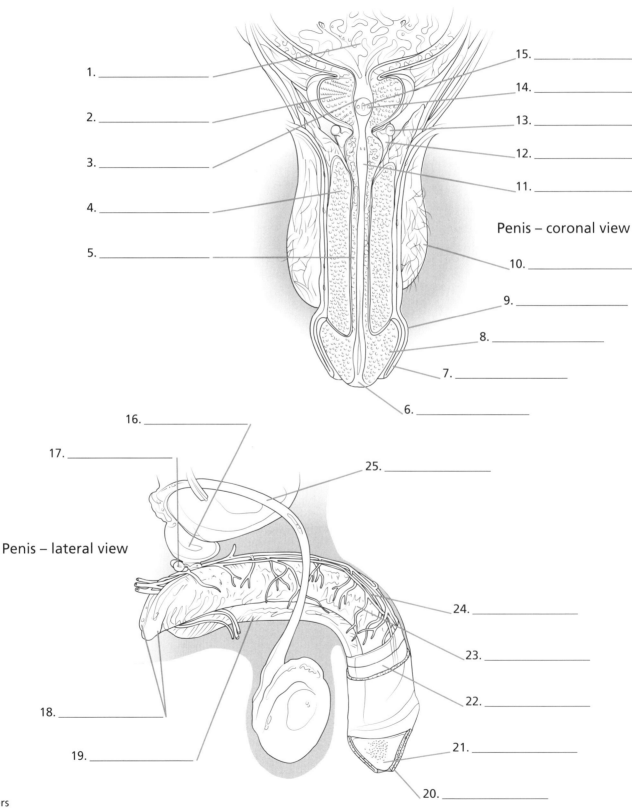

1. _____

2. _____

3. _____

4. _____

5. _____

15. _____

14. _____

13. _____

12. _____

11. _____

Penis – coronal view

10. _____

9. _____

8. _____

7. _____

6. _____

16. _____

17. _____

Penis – lateral view

25. _____

24. _____

23. _____

22. _____

21. _____

18. _____

19. _____

20. _____

Answers

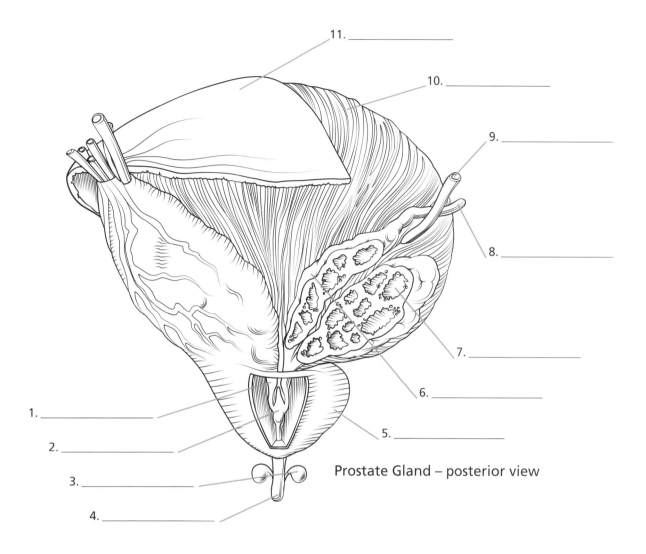

11. _____

10. _____

9. _____

8. _____

7. _____

6. _____

5. _____

1. _____

2. _____

3. _____

4. _____

Prostate Gland – posterior view

The penis is the external male reproductive and urinary organ through which semen and urine leave the body, and it is attached at its base to the pelvic bone by connective tissue. The penis is composed primarily of two cylinders of sponge-like vascular tissue (the corpora cavernosa) and a third cylinder (the corpus spongiosum) that contains the urethra, which carries both ejaculate and urine. The urethra ends at the glans, an external swelling at the tip of the penis. The glans is covered by the prepuce (foreskin). The prostate gland is shaped like an inverted pyramid and lies under the bladder, with the apex pointing downwards. All the glands of the prostate open into the prostatic urethra and secrete the enzyme acid phosphatase, fibrinolysin, and other proteins.

Carcinoma of the prostate

Cancer arising in the glands of the prostate is one of the most common types of cancer in the Western world. It usually arises in men older than 50, and the younger the age at which it appears, the more aggressive the cancer. Cancer screening by a blood test for prostate-specific antigen (PSA) is common, but remains controversial. The cancer usually originates in the peripheral parts of the gland, so feeling the size and consistency of the gland by digital rectal examination is a helpful diagnostic procedure. The cancer may spread to nearby bones (lumbar vertebrae) and lymph nodes.

Answers

1. Ejaculatory duct, 2. Prostatic urethra, 3. Bulbourethral gland, 4. Membranous urethra, 5. Prostate gland, 6. Ampulla of ductus deferens, 7. Seminal vesicle, 8. Ductus deferens, 9. Ureter, 10. Detrusor muscle (of bladder), 11. Peritoneum

Male Reproductive System and Organs

Testes – posterior view

1. _____

2. _____

9. _____

8. _____

7. _____

6. _____

5. _____

4. _____

3. _____

Sperm

10. _____

19. _____

18. _____

17. _____

15. _____

14. _____

13. _____

12. _____

16. _____

11. _____

32. _____

31. _____

30. _____

The testes, or testicles, are two ovoid organs contained in the scrotum, a sac that lies directly posterior to the penis. A central septum of the scrotum separates the testes. Each testis has a tough inelastic fibrous capsule called the tunica albuginea that sends partitions inwards to divide it into about 300 lobules. Each lobule contains coiled seminiferous tubules that converge into a network that sends about 20 small ducts through the tunica albuginea into the epididymis. The ducts become larger and convoluted and gradually fuse into the ductus deferens. Sperm are produced in the seminiferous tubules. The head of each sperm has a nucleus that contains chromosomes and an acrosomal membrane that holds enzymes needed for fertilisation. The tail of the sperm helps it move in a corkscrew action on its journey from the testes to the female reproductive organs.

20. _____

21. _____

22. _____

23. _____

24. _____

25. _____

26. _____

27. _____

28. _____

29. _____

Testes – structure

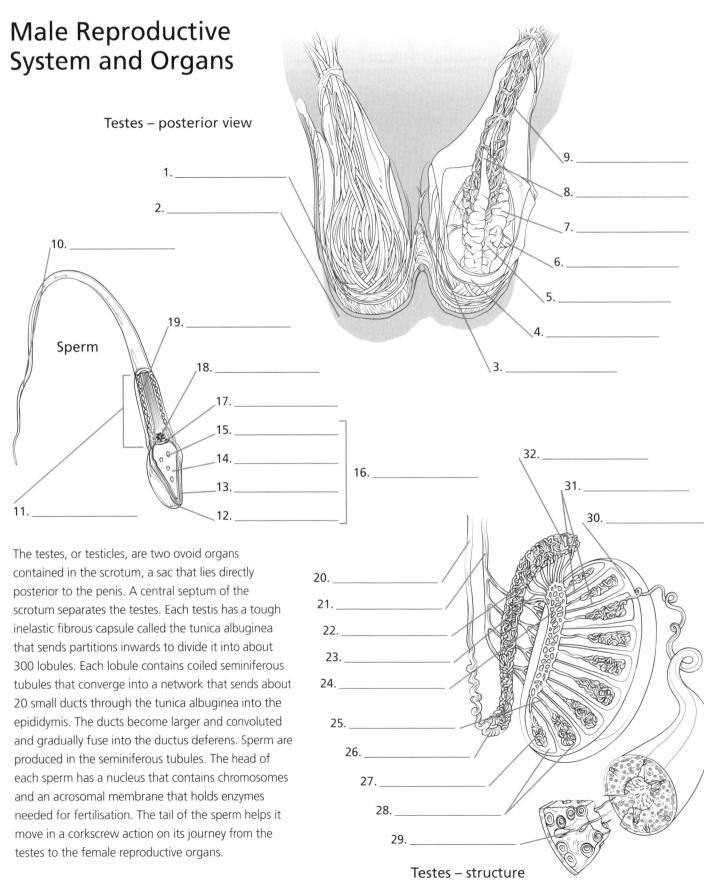

Answers

1. Superficial fascia of scrotum, 2. Scrotal skin, 3. Septum of scrotum, 4. Parietal layer of tunica vaginalis), 5. Body of epididymis, 6. Testis (covered by visceral layer of tunica vaginalis), 7. Head of epididymis, 8. Ductus deferens, 9. Pampiniform plexus of veins, 10. Tail, 11. Mitochondrial sheath (middle piece), 12. Cell membrane, 13. Acrosome, 14. Nucleus, 15. Nuclear vacuole, 16. Head, 17. Neck, 18. Centriole, 19. Mitochondrion, 20. Ductus deferens, 21. Testicular artery, 22. Body of epididymis, 23. Efferent ductules, 24. Rete testis, 25. Mediastinum testis, 26. Tail of epididymis, 27. Seminiferous tubules, 28. Lobules, 29. Spermatozoon, 30. Tunica albuginea, 31. Septae, 32. Head of epididymis

Female Reproductive System and Organs

1. _____
2. _____
3. _____
4. _____

Female Reproductive System – anterior view

Female Reproductive System – sagittal view

5. _____
6. _____
7. _____
8. _____
9. _____
10. _____

The female reproductive system includes two ovaries that produce ova and female hormones, two uterine tubes that convey the ova to the uterus, the uterus itself, and the vagina, which is connected to the external genitalia. The ovaries are almond-shaped and -sized organs located in the pelvis, situated just below the division of the common iliac arteries. Ova produced by the ovaries are 'captured' by the fimbriae of the uterine tubes, which open into the two top angles of the uterus. The upper two-thirds of the uterus – the body – rests on the bladder and has a very thick wall of smooth muscle. The lower third – the cervix – is a cylindrical muscular tube that protrudes into the vagina. The lumen of the cervix is a spindle-shaped canal. The vagina is a fibromuscular tube that runs from the cervix to the vestibule of the vulva.

Answers

Female Reproductive System and Organs

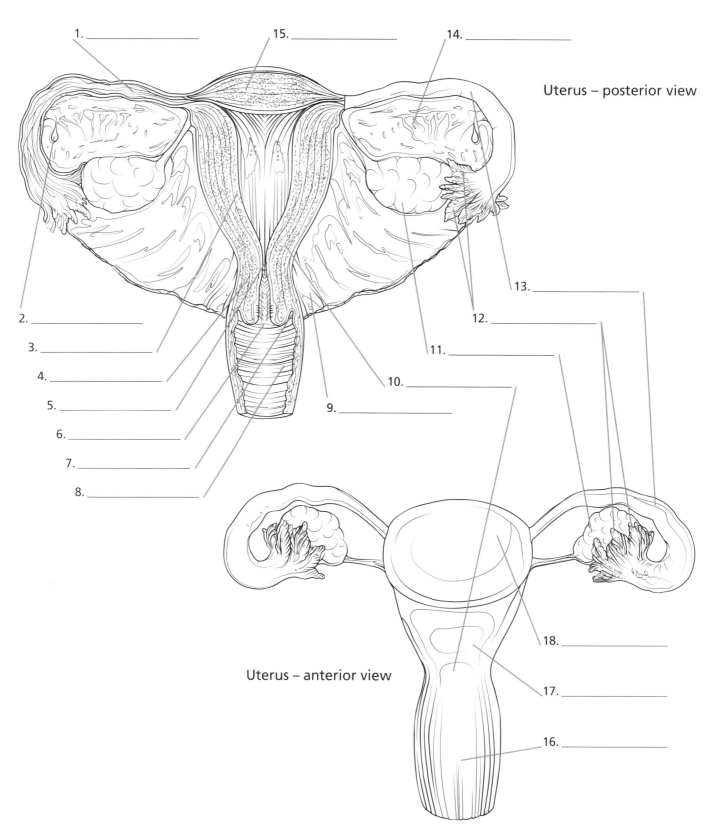

Uterus – posterior view

1. _____
15. _____
14. _____

2. _____
3. _____
4. _____
5. _____
6. _____
7. _____
8. _____

9. _____
10. _____
11. _____
12. _____
13. _____

Uterus – anterior view

18. _____
17. _____
16. _____

Answers

1. Uterine tube (cut open), 2. Hydatid of Morgagni, 3. Endometrium, 4. Myometrium, 5. Internal os of cervix, 6. External os of cervix, 7. Vaginal fornix (lateral), 8. Vagina, 9. Broad ligament, 10. Cervix, 11. Ovary, 12. Fimbriae, 13. Uterine tube, 14. Mesosalpinx (of broad ligament), 15. Fundus (of uterus), 16. Vagina, 17. Body (of uterus), 18. Fundus (of uterus)

External Genitalia – inferior view

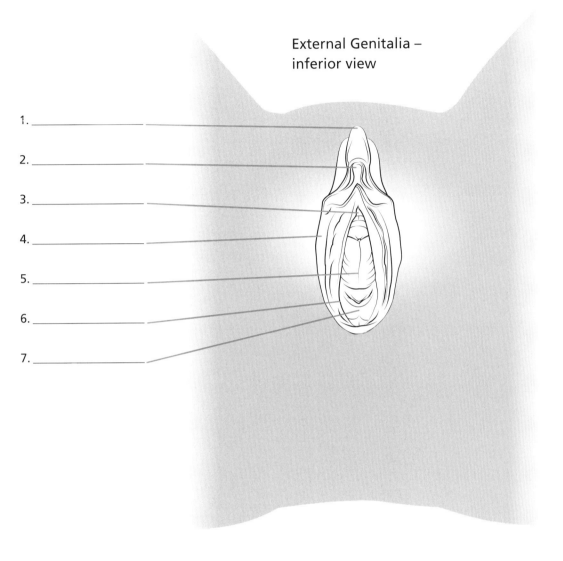

1. _____
2. _____
3. _____
4. _____
5. _____
6. _____
7. _____

The uterus is located in the pelvis. The uterine wall consists of the endometrium, myometrium, and perimetrium. The cervix is a cylindrical muscular tube that protrudes into the vagina and is surrounded by four fornices. The vagina is a fibromuscular tube that runs from the cervix to the vestibule of the vulva. The uterus is supported by the cervical ligaments, broad ligament, and pelvic floor muscles. The female external genitalia consist of paired folds, the labia majora. These join and continue superficially to the symphysis pubis as the mons pubis (mons veneris). The labia minora are folds within the labia majora that lie on either side of the vestibule containing the vaginal and urinary openings and the openings of the greater vestibular glands (Bartholin's glands).

Answers

1. Mons pubis, 2. Clitoris, 3. Orifice of urethra, 4. Labium majorum, 5. Orifice of vagina, 6. Labium minorum, 7. Hymen

Female Reproductive System and Organs

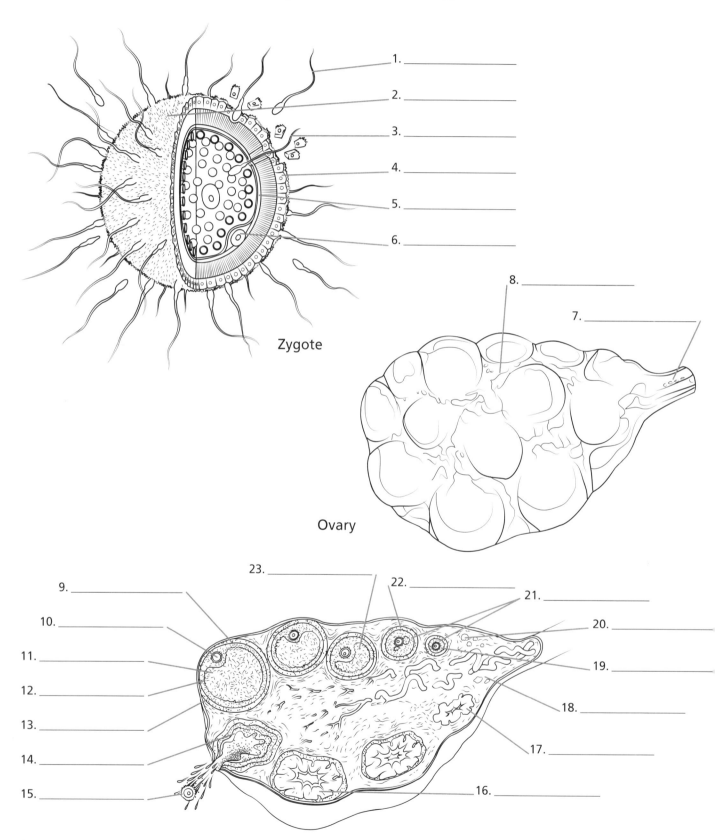

1. _____

2. _____

3. _____

4. _____

5. _____

6. _____

Zygote

8. _____

7. _____

Ovary

23. _____

22. _____

21. _____

9. _____

10. _____

20. _____

11. _____

19. _____

12. _____

18. _____

13. _____

17. _____

14. _____

15. _____

16. _____

Answers

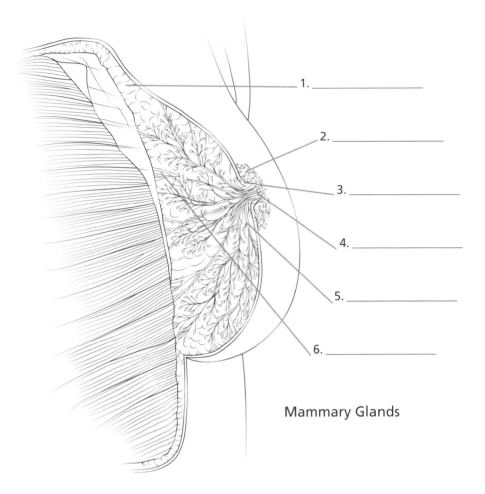

Mammary Glands

1. _____
2. _____
3. _____
4. _____
5. _____
6. _____

A zygote is the cell created when a sperm enters and fertilises an ovum, before the process of division begins. Beneath the surface epithelium of the ovary is the cortex, which encloses the medulla at its core. The bulk of the ovary is a supporting structure called the stroma. The cortex contains ova at different stages of development. The breasts, or mammary glands, are located on the chest. They are composed mainly of adipose (fat) cells, interspersed with sac-like lobules. These lobules are glands that can produce milk in females when stimulated by hormones such as prolactin. The lobules empty into a network of ducts that transport milk from the lobules to the nipple. During puberty, the sex hormone oestrogen causes the breasts to grow in size, due to the laying down of fat deposits.

Polycystic ovary syndrome

This condition is due to excessive levels of the steroid hormones called androgens. These hormones induce male characteristics, but are also present in healthy women. Women with excess levels of androgens experience acne; difficulty getting pregnant; heavy, irregular, or absent periods; and excess hair on the body and face. Risk factors include family history, obesity, and insufficient exercise. The condition is named for the cysts that may develop on the ovaries and which can be seen with ultrasound. Treatment is by weight loss, exercise, oral contraceptives, and medications to treat the acne and infertility.

Answers
1. Adipose tissue, 2. Areola, 3. Nipple, 4. Lactiferous duct, 5. Lactiferous sinus, 6. Fibrocollagenous septa (Cooper's suspensory ligament)

Fetal Skull Development

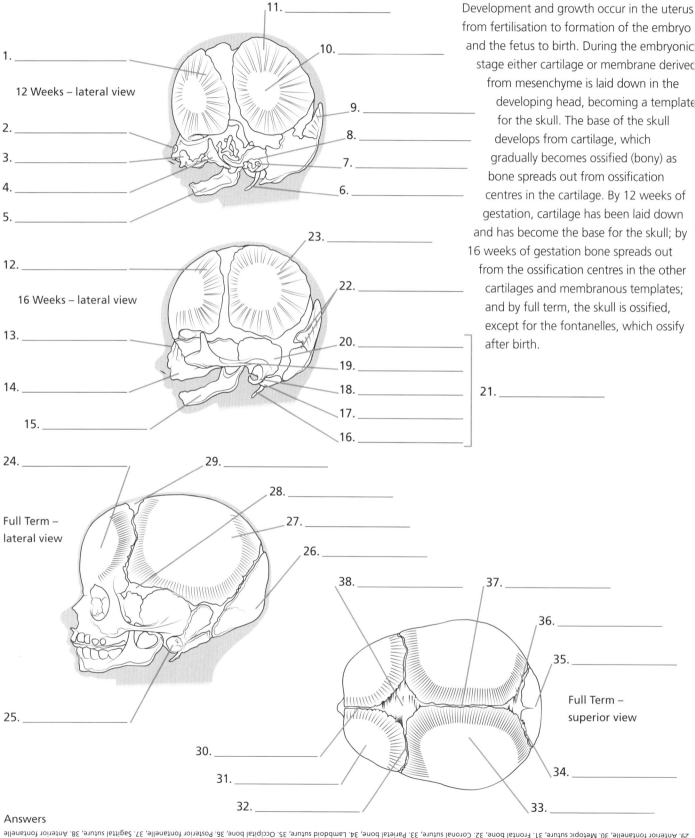

1. _____

12 Weeks – lateral view

2. _____

3. _____

4. _____

5. _____

11. _____

10. _____

9. _____

8. _____

7. _____

6. _____

12. _____

16 Weeks – lateral view

13. _____

14. _____

15. _____

23. _____

22. _____

20. _____

19. _____

18. _____

17. _____

16. _____

21. _____

24. _____

Full Term – lateral view

25. _____

29. _____

28. _____

27. _____

26. _____

30. _____

31. _____

32. _____

38. _____

37. _____

36. _____

35. _____

Full Term – superior view

34. _____

33. _____

Development and growth occur in the uterus from fertilisation to formation of the embryo and the fetus to birth. During the embryonic stage either cartilage or membrane derived from mesenchyme is laid down in the developing head, becoming a template for the skull. The base of the skull develops from cartilage, which gradually becomes ossified (bony) as bone spreads out from ossification centres in the cartilage. By 12 weeks of gestation, cartilage has been laid down and has become the base for the skull; by 16 weeks of gestation bone spreads out from the ossification centres in the other cartilages and membranous templates; and by full term, the skull is ossified, except for the fontanelles, which ossify after birth.

Answers

1. Frontal bone, 2. Nasal bone, 3. Maxilla, 4. Zygomatic bone, 5. Mandible, 6. Styloid process, 7. Tympanic ring, 8. Squamous part of temporal bone, 9. Squamous part of occipital bone, 10. Parietal eminence, 11. Parietal bone, 12. Frontal bone, 13. Nasal bone, 14. Maxilla, 15. Mandible, 16. Styloid process, 17. Mastoid part of temporal bone, 18. Tympanic ring, 19. Zygomatic process, 20. Squamous part of temporal bone, 21. Temporal bone, 22. Occipital bone, 23. Parietal bone, 24. Frontal bone, 25. External acoustic meatus, 26. Occipital bone, 27. Parietal bone, 28. Pterion, 29. Anterior fontanelle, 30. Metopic suture, 31. Frontal bone, 32. Coronal suture, 33. Parietal bone, 34. Lambdoid suture, 35. Occipital bone, 36. Posterior fontanelle, 37. Sagittal suture, 38. Anterior fontanelle

Bone Development

1. _____

2. _____

3. _____

4. _____

5. _____

6. _____

Bone Growth

Long bones begin as cartilage models in the embryo. Chondrocytes secrete cartilage matrix, leading to mature cartilage. By birth, ossification (development of bone) has reached almost to the articular ends (epiphyses) of the cartilage models. New centres of bone growth also form in the articular ends of the developing long bones. A plate of cartilage (a growth plate) persists along the leading edge of ossification and is responsible for lengthening of the developing long bones. The growth plate moves steadily away from the centre of the bone towards the ends until all the cartilage has ossified. Growth in bone length is then complete. By the age of about 20, ossification reaches and includes the growth plate, at which time growth stops.

Answers

Index

Major topics are indicated with **bold** page numbers.